PERIODIC CLASSIFICATION OF THE ELEMENTS

(BASED ON $C^{12} = 12.0000$)

1961 ATOMIC WEIGHTS

Light Metals

Nonmetals

Heavy Metals

IA	IIA		IIIB	IVB	VB	VIB	VIIB		VIIIB		IB	IIB	IIIA	IVA	VA	VIA	VIIA	VIIIA
1 H 1.0080																		2 He 4.003
3 Li 6.939	4 Be 9.012												5 B 10.81	6 C 12.011	7 N 14.007	8 O 15.9994	9 F 18.998	10 Ne 20.183
11 Na 22.990	12 Mg 24.31												13 Al 26.98	14 Si 28.09	15 P 30.974	16 S 32.064	17 Cl 35.453	18 Ar 39.948
19 K 39.102	20 Ca 40.08		21 Sc 44.96	22 Ti 47.90	23 V 50.94	24 Cr 52.00	25 Mn 54.94	26 Fe 55.85	27 Co 58.93	28 Ni 58.71	29 Cu 63.54	30 Zn 65.37	31 Ga 69.72	32 Ge 72.59	33 As 74.92	34 Se 78.96	35 Br 79.909	36 Kr 83.80
37 Rb 85.47	38 Sr 87.62		39 Y 88.91	40 Zr 91.22	41 Nb 92.91	42 Mo 95.94	43 Tc (99)	44 Ru 101.1	45 Rh 102.90	46 Pd 106.4	47 Ag 107.870	48 Cd 112.40	49 In 114.82	50 Sn 118.69	51 Sb 121.75	52 Te 127.60	53 I 126.90	54 Xe 131.30
55 Cs 132.91	56 Ba 137.34		57 TO 71	72 Hf 178.49	73 Ta 180.95	74 W 183.85	75 Re 186.2	76 Os 190.2	77 Ir 192.2	78 Pt 195.09	79 Au 197.0	80 Hg 200.59	81 Tl 204.37	82 Pb 207.19	83 Bi 208.98	84 Po (210)	85 At (210)	86 Rn (222)
87 Fr (223)	88 Ra 226.05		89 TO 103															

Lanthanide series	57 La 138.91	58 Ce 140.12	59 Pr 140.91	60 Nd 144.24	61 Pm (147)	62 Sm 150.35	63 Eu 151.96	64 Gd 157.25	65 Tb 158.92	66 Dy 162.50	67 Ho 164.93	68 Er 167.26	69 Tm 168.93	70 Yb 173.04	71 Lu 174.97
Actinide series	89 Ac (227)	90 Th 232.04	91 Pa (231)	92 U 238.03	93 Np (237)	94 Pu (242)	95 Am (243)	96 Cm (247)	97 Bk (249)	98 Cf (251)	99 Es (254)	100 Fm (253)	101 Md (256)	102 No (254)	103 Lw (257)

Chemistry

John S. McAnally

Occidental College

CHARLES E. MERRILL BOOKS, INC., COLUMBUS, OHIO

Merrill Physical Science Series

Robert J. Foster and Walter A. Gong, *Editors*

San Jose State College

Library of Congress Catalog Card Number: 66-18752

PRINTED IN THE UNITED STATES OF AMERICA

Editors' Foreword

As curricula become more crowded in this age of rapidly expanding knowledge and specialization, more and more colleges and universities are turning to integrated interdisciplinary courses to transmit the basic essentials of science to non-science majors. We believe that the rigid structure of most physical science textbooks has imposed severe limitations on instruction in these courses. Far too often, instructors trained in various specialities have had to attempt to fit the wide range of goals, abilities, and backgrounds of their students to a textbook, when the converse, of course, would be much more satisfactory.

In January, 1965, the editors, five authors, and representatives of Charles E. Merrill Books, Inc., met in San Francisco to implement a new conception of physical science textbooks. The result is the *Physical Science Series,* a collection of specially written, integrated materials in short, paperback form for the college physical science program. Our coordinated efforts were directed by three vital principles.

1. The Series permits maximum flexibility of use by instructors and students. Each paperback textbook represents a five-to-seven-week section of instruction, and may be used in any sequence or combination desired by the instructor. In addition, freedom of sequence within a single book is possible. This flexibility is especially helpful in courses that include laboratory experience. In this way it is hoped that each instructor will be free to choose the most appropriate materials for his students.

2. The subject areas are portrayed in a valid manner. Each book is written by a specialist in a different discipline—physicist, chemist, astronomer, meteorologist, geologist, and science educator. Thus, in place of a homogeneous blend of textbook statements, the individual paperback textbooks have distinctive scientific flavors. The student can discover both the contrasts and underlying unities in the viewpoints of scientists in different disciplines; he can, for example, compare the approach of the physicist, who performs lab-

iii

oratory experiments, with that of the geologist, who depends largely on observations of natural occurrences.

3. Scientific communication is clear, concise, and correct. Each author is both academician and experienced teacher. He has designed instruction around carefully selected scientific principles logically related to laws, definitions, and associated phenomena. Technology is used to provide illustrative examples rather than a myriad of facts to be remembered. Mathematical reasoning is used only when the sciences are made more (not less) understandable for the non-science major. Scientific jargon and excessive nomenclature are avoided.

San Jose, California   *Robert J. Foster*

                                                         Walter A. Gong

Table of Contents

Chapter 1

Solids, Liquids, and Gases

As we look at the physical universe around us and the myriad of qualitatively different materials with which chemistry must concern itself, we are faced with the problem of creating some degree of order among our impressions. The beginnings of any science are characterized by attempts to classify information, seeking out the likenesses among seemingly dissimilar things. It is necessary to interpret the sensations that are received from objects because, even though every scientist must depend to some degree upon common sense, the science must very early in its development transcend common sense impressions and conceptions. Yet we must always remember that every science is based upon an unproved and unprovable assumption: that the universe is an orderly one.

1-1 The States of Matter

An initial description and classification of matter can be accomplished with relative ease by observing the state in which the matter exists. With only a few exceptions, all things of the macroscopic world—those things which man can see and touch—can be included in one of three general groups: *solid, liquid* or *gas*. This sort of grouping is made on the basis of sensations, and it is clear that this is all that we have to initiate our study of matter. By common consent, these three words represent a spectrum of physical properties that are possessed to a greater or lesser degree by each of the items which we classify. Intuitively knowing what each of these words means, however, is not sufficient. It is mandatory that we define the terms so that there can be no possibility of misunderstanding, so that the classification is more than a recognition. Before we can begin to consider the three states of matter, we must establish the meaning of the term *matter* itself. In the everyday world, this is not particularly difficult if we simply iterate that matter is anything which we can characterize by its physical dimensions. As a corollary, we can apply the specific term *mass*. Now mass does not mean weight.

Recent tentative explorations outside the earth's atmosphere have made weightlessness a common concept of our time, and yet we all accept the idea that the disappearance of weight does not result in the disappearance of mass; the mass is still in existence, but one of the commonly employed parameters for describing it has ceased to be meaningful. What then is left to use in describing and classifying the states of matter? Within the framework that we will establish, only two concepts are required: shape and volume.

If we look around us, we note a great many objects that have both a definite shape and a definite volume. It is true that there are a great many different shapes and different volumes, but for many individual objects the shape and the volume are invariable so long as nothing is done to disturb the entity; these objects we group together in the class of *solids*. The *liquid* is distinguished from the solid by its lack of rigidity. While a quantity of liquid has a fixed volume under a given set of conditions, the shape is not a property of the liquid but is determined by the shape of the solid vessel in which it is contained. The third state of matter has an evanescent quality, which caused it to remain undiscovered for centuries after man began to speculate about the composition of his immediate surroundings. A *gas* has no fixed volume, it expands to fill the volume of the container, and since it fills completely any closed container into which it is placed, it has no definite shape. Only a little more than three hundred years ago did technology advance to the point that experimental scientists were able to determine something of the properties of matter in the gaseous state, and to recognize that three distinct states of matter existed.

When we consider the three states of matter, our experience tells us that the existence of matter in any one of the states depends upon the conditions to which it is subjected. By "conditions" is meant, of course, the environmental conditions that are susceptible to experimental variation. Pressure and temperature are the factors that determine, to a considerable degree, the physical state of matter—for example, water in the gaseous, liquid or solid state. However, because liquids and solids give no noticeable, uniform response to small changes in temperature or pressure, scientific investigation of the effects of changes in these factors was not possible until the invention of tools that enabled scientists to carry out experiments with gases.

1-2   The Concept of Pressure

It is necessary to distinguish clearly between the meanings of the terms *pressure* and total pressure, or *force*. The physicist finds it very easy to define these terms precisely, but we will apply a common-sense analogy which is rather easily understood, but which does not provide an exact meaning. Total force means total push. If we imagine a horizontal surface upon which some object is resting, the total force exerted downward will be the weight of the object. The pressure will be the total force (or weight) divided by the area covered by the object, so that we express the weight on each unit of area. (Certain experiments which we will consider later will demonstrate conclusively that this elementary attempt at definition is not sufficient.) The pressure that a sample of matter exerts depends upon its physical state. The rigidity of a solid is great enough that the solid does not alter its shape. It exerts a pressure downward. A liquid has no definite shape and tends to fill its container. Then it is exerting pressure downward and outward as it attempts to distort the container. Since the pressure in a liquid is a measure of the weight of the matter above a given level, the pressure increases as the depth of the liquid increases.

Gases have no definite shape, but attempt to expand in all directions. The container then must exert a total force and force per unit area (or pressure), inward, of exactly the same magnitude as the total force (and pressure) exerted outward by the confined gas. If the pressure is maintained, the situation remains unchanged. However, what will occur if the pressure on a *fluid* (a liquid or a gas) is increased? If the pressure on a liquid is increased, there is a small decrease in volume. This change is so small that little of significance could be learned from it in the 17th-century laboratory. The results which could be obtained with solids were even more equivocal. But beginning about 1620, chemists and physicists carried out a number of investigations which marked what can almost be called the dawn of experimental science. Torricelli, Pascal, Boyle and von Guericke were among those who made the contributions of greatest significance.

Historically we are, or course, indebted to Robert Boyle for the law describing the behavior of gases in response to changes in pressure. But Boyle was able to proceed with his investigations only because of the prior work of those who had demonstrated experimentally a rational basis for the belief that a sea of air of considerable weight envelopes the earth and exerts a pressure upon the surface which is related to the thickness of the gas blanket.

Measurement of the pressure exerted by the air was first accomplished by Torricelli with his mercury barometer. This first barometer was nothing more than a glass tube, sealed at one end and filled with mercury. This tube was inverted carefully so that none of the mercury escaped, and the open end was placed below the surface of a quantity of mercury in a dish. It was then found that when the length of the tube above the mercury in the dish was greater than about thirty inches, the height of the column of mercury would fall until it reached that level. The conclusion drawn was that since the space above the mercury in the tube was a vacuum (a space devoid of air), the pressure exerted downward by the mercury in the tube was just balanced by thte pressure of the air on the mercury in the dish. Pascal then was instrumental in having a barometer carried from the bottom of a mountain to the top, reasoning correctly that if what was being measured was truly the pressure of the atmosphere, the measurement on the top of the peak would be less than that at the bottom. However, both Torricelli and Pascal left several important questions unanswered, questions which Boyle proposed to investigate. It was difficult in the beginning to make a distinction between weight and pressure. It was necessary to establish some difference, otherwise it would not be possible to explain why the mercury column did not fall when the mercury reservoir was enclosed in an airtight box and the total weight of the "sea of air" no longer bore down upon the surface of the mercury.

1-3   The Development of Boyle's Law

One of the early experiments carried out by Boyle was the evacuation of a globe containing a barometer, using an air pump which he had invented. With this relatively crude pump, Boyle was able to reduce the pressure sufficiently so that the mercury column fell until it was no more than one-quarter inch in height. It was easily demonstrable that the air pumped from the globe did not weigh as much as the mercury in the column; thus it was a logical step to divorce the concepts of weight and pressure, since the support for the column of mercury did not come from an equal weight of air. Now Boyle reversed the pump and increased the air pressure inside the globe and found that the height of the column of mercury could be increased above its original value. A variety of other experiments were performed with this rudimentary equipment. The one which concerns us most is that which provided the basis for the law which bears Boyle's name.

The law relating the volume of a sample of gas to the pressure to which the gas is subjected was proposed after a series of measurements were made on the gas confined in the short, closed arm of a J-shaped tube. The first step was to introduce a quantity of mercury into the longer, open end of the tube so that the air in the closed end could not escape. Just enough mercury was added to bring the levels in the two arms to the same height. Now Boyle added successive increments of mercury into the open end of the tube. The result of these additions was a decrease in the volume of the confined gas. Measurement of the distance from the mercury level in the closed tube to the level in the open tube allowed the calculation of the total pressure (P) to which the gas was subjected (Fig. 1-1). When the data was examined, it was found that there was an inverse relationship between the volume of the gas (V) and the height of the column of mercury, as is shown in Table 1-1. Within the limits of experimental error, it was found that *pressure* $\times$ *volume* equaled a constant $(PV = K)$. This equality is mathematically true only if the temperature of the gas remains constant. If the temperature is raised or lowered, we must substitute a new value for the constant K. It was perhaps fortunate that the laboratory equipment with which Boyle had to work was relatively crude. If it had not been, the unrecognized factors affecting the experiment might have introduced variations great enough to obscure the relationship which he noticed. As is true with so many of the generalizations

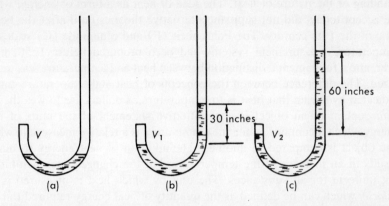

Fig. 1-1. Change in volume of gas with increasing pressure. In (a) the pressure *P* is the atmospheric pressure, equal to 30 inches of mercury. In (b) and (c) atmospheric pressure is added to the difference in the mercury levels.

Table 1-1

	P (in. of Hg)	V (cc)	PV
(a)	30	60	1,800
(b)	60	30	1,800
(c)	90	20	1,800

which we call "scientific laws," the mathematical equations must be modified as the data are more precisely measured. From the data which he was able to collect, Boyle constructed the concept of the relation of volume to pressure. Certainly he did not establish a law. Only after the physical system has been investigated from many different aspects, and only after the generalization has become well established by virtue of never having been found to be incorrect under a carefully defined set of conditions, do we dignify the statement predicting the behavior of the system by calling it a "law." Mathematically Boyle's law is $PV = P'V'$, and it can be given verbally by saying that so long as the temperature remains constant, the volume of a gas is inversely proportional to the pressure.

1-4 Heat and Temperature

When Boyle was performing experiments with gases it is doubtful that he gave any consideration to the temperature at which his manipulations were carried out. Not until more than one hundred years later was a theory put forward which related changes of gas volume to changes in temperature. This lapse of time was probably due in great part to the imperfect understanding of the nature of heat. The idea of heat as a form of energy, which we accept today, did not supplant alternative theories until after the beginning of the 19th century. The Fahrenheit (F) and centigrade (C) scales for temperature measurement systems had been proposed before 1750, however, and a fundamental distinction between heat and temperature was recognized. The difference between the concepts of heat and temperature can be indicated by saying that heat is to temperature as dollars are to wealth. The *heat* content of an object is a quantitative statement of the units of heat energy which it contains, while the *temperature* is a relative measure in which one object is compared to another. The addition of heat energy to matter results in an increase in the temperature, but the change in temperature is not uniform for all substances. The unit by which heat is measured is the *calorie,* which can be defined as the quantity of heat energy required to raise the temperature of one gram of water one degree centigrade. The heat capacity of any substance is the quantity of heat required to raise the temperature of one gram one degree centigrade.

If we could gradually remove the heat from an object until no more remained, the ultimate in low temperature—*absolute zero*—would be attained. This total absence of heat forms the basis for the system of temperature measurement known as the Kelvin (K), or absolute scale. This temperature scale uses the same divisions as the centigrade; that is, there are 100 divisions between the freezing point and the boiling point of water. Since absolute zero is —273° centigrade, the numerical values of these two reference points are 273 and 373, respectively. It is in terms of this scale that the relation of the temperature to the volume of a sample of a gas can be established, since all numerical values for temperature are positive numbers.

1-5   *Temperature Change and Charles' Law*

If a gas is heated, its volume becomes greater. This can be demonstrated easily by exposing a filled toy balloon to different temperatures. Of course, the tension of the rubber becomes greater as the size increases, so no quantitative study can be made, but if we confine a sample of a gas in a cylinder with a freely moving yet gas-tight piston, we can make the necessary measurements. In such an experimental apparatus, the volume of the gas will be determined by the atmospheric pressure and the weight of the piston. The pressure inside the cylinder will be constant so long as there is no change in the quantity of gas or the outside pressure. Raising the temperature of the gas will result in an increase in the volume (Fig. 1-2), but the pressure on the gas will remain unchanged because the piston is free to move. If the data collected by measuring the volume at different temperatures are studied, it is noted that the volume is directly proportional to the temperature, or $V/T =$ constant (see Table 1-2).

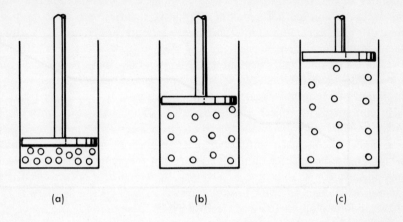

(a)   (b)   (c)

Fig. 1-2. As the temperature increases, the volume of the confined gas increases.

Table 1-2

	T (Kelvin, or absolute, scale)	V (cc)	V/T
(a)	300	50	1/6
(b)	600	100	1/6
(c)	1,200	200	1/6

1-6 The Effect of Temperature Change on Solids and Liquids

The responses of solids and liquids to changes in temperature appear to be almost capricious, although most substances do expand when their heat content is increased. Of course, solids and liquids are susceptible to variations in volume with changes in temperature; they can, and do, undergo changes in state. If heat is added to a block of ice, beginning at 253°K (—20°C), the temperature rises gradually until it reaches 273°K. At this point, the continued introduction of energy does not cause a further increase in temperature; rather there is a gradual change from the solid to the liquid state. This transformation does not occur instantaneously (Fig. 1-3). A large quantity of energy must be added for each gram of matter that is so altered. The number of calories required to melt one gram of any solid, without any increase in temperature, is termed the *heat of fusion*. If a liquid boils —that is, if the change is from the liquid to the gaseous state—the quantity of heat absorbed per gram is termed the *heat of vaporization*. The values ob-

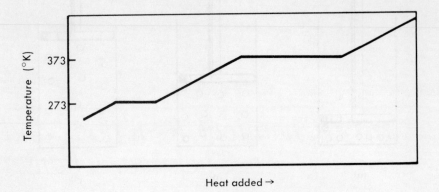

Fig. 1-3. **Temperature as a function of added heat in the ice-water-steam system.**

served are characteristic of the substance under investigation, and we will see later the implications of these observations for our investiagtions into the organization of matter on the submicroscopic level.

QUESTIONS FOR STUDY AND REVIEW

1. Gold can be hammered into thin sheets, and copper can be drawn into fine wires. How can we fit these observations into our definition of a solid?

2. If mercury is 13.6 times as heavy as water, how high would a water barometer be if it were constructed in the design used by Torricelli? How does this relate to the height to which water can be lifted by a suction pump?

3. Balloons are often used to lift scientific instruments to heights of over 100,000 feet. What is the implication of Pascal's experiment with a barometer for this operation?

4. How does a scientific law, such as Boyle's law, differ in concept and application from a law established by a legislative body?

5. An equation for converting temperature on the Fahrenheit scale to °C is $C = \frac{5}{9} (F - 32)$. What is the value of absolute zero on the Fahrenheit scale? At what temperature would the two scales have the same reading?

6. A desert water bag is made of canvas, and water seeps gradually to the outer surface. How is this system effective in supplying the traveler with cool water to drink?

Chapter 2

Chemical Reactions and Chemical Change

In addition to those physical properties which are used to classify matter, there are also characteristics of a different nature which allow much finer distinctions to be drawn. If the chemical properties of a given material are elucidated, it is possible to discover a unique set for every individual type. These *chemical properties* differ from *physical properties* in that the former are statements about the manner in which one kind of matter interacts with others, while the latter are descriptive of what the material is, in and of itself.

Chemical reactions always result in the disappearance of those entities which interact (the reactants) and the appearance of one or more new substances with different properties (the products). Chemical change is distinguished from a change of physical state in that it cannot be readily reversed by a return to the original environmental conditions. Additionally, and most importantly, chemical properties are independent of physical form, although the speeds with which reactions occur may be profoundly affected by alterations in the physical state of the substances involved. Quantitative studies of chemical changes are necessary and important, but before those are considered we must define more carefully the classes of materials with which we will be dealing.

2-1 *Classification of Matter*

Thus far, we have used nonspecific terms to identify samples of matter, but a study of chemical reactions quickly indicates that subdivision into groups is possible. Even a rather cursory examination of our surroundings shows that some solid objects are homogeneous and others are heterogeneous. The distinction is less easily made with matter in the liquid and the gaseous states, but even here it is usually possible by physical means to identify and separate heterogeneous samples into two or more components. If such a separation by physical means is possible, we describe the original system as a *mixture,* and the homogeneous materials separated from it are substances. Mixtures generally are not uniform in composition since the particles of which they are composed are of appreciable size. The exception to this statement is found in that type of mixture which we call a *solution.* In this case the smallest particles of the dispersing phase (the *solvent*) and of the dispersed phase (the *solute*) are submicroscopic in size and the solution appears to be homogeneous. The mere appearance of homogeneity is not the deciding factor, however, and solutions are classed as mixtures because they can be separated by physical means into individual substances.

Those materials which are homogeneous in both physical and chemical properties are divided into two classes. Substances which can be resolved into two or more constituents, or which are formed by the chemical combination of two or more other substances, are called *compounds.* Those which cannot be broken down by chemical means are termed *elementary substances* or *elements.* As we study the development of the atomic theory we will see that there are means other than chemical analysis for identifying elements and compounds, but the definitions given above are sufficient for most aspects of the study of chemistry.

2-2 The Conservation of Mass

Verbal descriptions of chemical reactions are of limited usefulness, and chemistry as a science did not develop rapidly until attention was directed to their quantitative aspects. It was early in the 18th century that serious consideration was given to the relation of the weights of the reactants and the products of a chemical reaction. Many chemical reactions were well known, but these were principally in the province of the artisans of the day. To these men chemical changes were means to ends, and the guild member was concerned with practical results. The consideration of two types of reactions, combustion and calcination, led eventually to such confusion that only a systematic study could clarify the problem.

Everyday experience demonstrated that the process of *combustion* (the burning of fuels) resulted in a decrease in mass, but equally evident was the increase in weight that occurred when a metal such as zinc was heated in air (*calcination*). At this time nothing was known of the composition of the atmosphere, and there was no logical theory that could encompass both of these observations. Not until the discovery of oxygen by Priestley and carbon dioxide by Black was any quantitative study possible. Technology then had progressed to the extent that confined samples of gases could be handled readily, and Priestley showed conclusively that oxygen was the component of the air that was involved in the reactions of combustion and calcination; it was also demonstrated that one product of combustion was the gas carbon dioxide. When gases were shown to have mass, the stage was set for the establishment of the *Law of Conservation of Mass* in chemical reactions. Without this law there could have been no beginning of the science of chemistry, because there could be no systematic study of reactions with regard to both products and reactants.

The unequivocal demonstration of the fact that mass was conserved was carried out by Antoine Lavoisier. The experiments were simple ones, but their importance cannot be overstated. The reactions which Lavoisier studied were the formation and decomposition of two compounds: mercury and oxygen, and tin and oxygen. When mercury is heated in air at a relatively low temperature, a red film of mercuric oxide forms on the surface, and when the temperature is raised the oxide decomposes and the metal and the gas are reformed. Lavoisier heated a sample of mercury for twelve days in a closed system and found that the volume of air decreased by a small volume. When the red oxide was carefully collected and was heated to a higher temperature it was decomposed, and the volume of gas formed was equal to the volume which had disappeared in the process of formation of the compound. The gas which remained after the initial reaction was shown to be incapable of supporting combustion. That which was collected after the decomposition of the red oxide was shown to be oxygen, and the mixing of the gas samples produced a gas which was indistinguishable from air. From this beginning, a second experiment was devised which would measure quantitatively the weight changes that took place in the course of a chemical reaction.

A sample of tin was placed in a retort (a glass vessel with a bulbous body and an extended neck), and the vessel and contents were warmed. The air expanded, and while the vessel was warm, the neck was sealed off. This procedure was necessary to prevent the breaking of the retort when it was heated more strongly. The weight of the tin, container, and air had been determined, both before heating and after heating and sealing. The container was then heated strongly, and a black oxide of tin formed on the surface of the metal. When the retort was weighed, it was found that there had been no increase in weight, but when the sealed end of the retort was broken so that air could re-enter, it was discovered that the weight had increased. A comparison of the weight of the tin oxide plus that of the unreacted tin with that of the metal originally introduced into the retort showed that the metal had gained the same amount as had metal, retort and air. It was evident that the increase in weight was due to the reaction between the metal and the oxygen of the air. Thus, by two different means—measurement of gas volume and of weight of product—Lavoisier had demonstrated that matter was indeed conserved in chemical reactions.

2-3 The Law of Definite Proportions

Lavoisier's career came to a tragic end at the guillotine in the French Revolution, but the ideas which he had generated were followed up and expanded upon by others. A series of measurements made by Joseph Proust produced data which made possible the statement of the *Law of Definite Proportions*. Samples of varying size of the same compound were studied, and it was found that the proportions by weight of the elements in the compound did not vary. When these observations were extended to cover several compounds, it was found that the same conclusion could be drawn no matter what the identity of the original compound.

Consideration of these two discoveries—the Law of Conservation of Mass and the Law of Definite Proportions—led John Dalton to the enunciation of his *Atomic Theory*. The work of many experimental scientists provided the data that allowed this theoretician to construct the theory which was to be so fruitful in stimulating additional investigations. The science of chemistry had progressed to the point where it could support professional practitioners, a circumstance that had not existed in the 18th century. The foundations of chemistry were laid by men such as Joseph Black (a physician), Joseph Priestley (a Unitarian preacher), Antoine Lavoisier (a tax collector and public servant), and a host of others for whom science was an avocation. But now the scene was to be taken over by teachers and professors—Proust, Dalton, Berthelot, Avogadro and many more. In the next chapter, we shall see how Dalton's theory established the basis for the development of the modern science of chemistry.

QUESTIONS FOR STUDY AND REVIEW

1. What distinguishes chemical properties from physical properties? In what category would taste, odor, and flexibility be?

2. We often speak of quality versus quantity in everyday affairs. What do the terms qualitative and quantitative mean in science?

3. Definitions of terms are always important in chemistry. What types of matter are mercury, table salt, soil, and a chair?

4. The Law of Conservation of Mass was soon changed to the Law of Conservation of Mass and Energy. This truth has been demonstrated by the Atomic Age. How does an atomic explosion illustrate this law?

5. A one-gram sample of water was found to contain two parts hydrogen to one part oxygen. According to the Law of Definite Proportions, can you say what the ratio of hydrogen to oxygen will be in the water in a quart of milk?

6. Speculate on the state of science if there were no Law of Definite Proportions.

Chapter 3

The Atomic Theory

The idea that matter might be made up of ultimately indivisible particles is not a new one. Two schools of thought grew up in early Greek science, one of which suggested that if it were possible to divide a macroscopic sample indefinitely, there would come a time at which division would no longer be possible. Unfortunately, the view put forward by Aristotle that *qualities* were of ultimate importance was given the greater credibility, and for almost two thousand years matter was considered infinitely divisible. Of course, it must be recognized that the argument was a philosophical one, because there was no experimental evidence to support either concept against the other. In fact, this argument points up the inherent weakness that existed in Greek and medieval science: disagreements were never based on operational techniques but, rather, were speculative in nature. It must be conceded that the idea of atoms continually reoccurred, but since no experimental evidence was collected, the concept regularly degenerated into nothing more than a matter of choice. The theorizing of John Dalton marked the real break with the speculation of the past, as Dalton based his assumptions on the experimental evidence collected by the laboratory workers of the 18th century. The work of such men as Lavoisier and Priestley furnished the data which inspired the country school teacher to make scientific deductions on the ultimate nature of matter.

3-1 John Dalton and the Atomic Theory

The observations that formed the basis for Dalton's Atomic Theory were of two sorts: Lavoisier had demonstrated unequivocally that mass (weight) was conserved in chemical reactions, and Proust had shown with equal clarity that compounds did have a definite and regular composition. Dalton reasoned, in the light of these two statements, that atomicity was a necessary corollary, and he enunciated a theory of the structure of matter which took into account all of the evidence available up to that date. We must recognize that in the

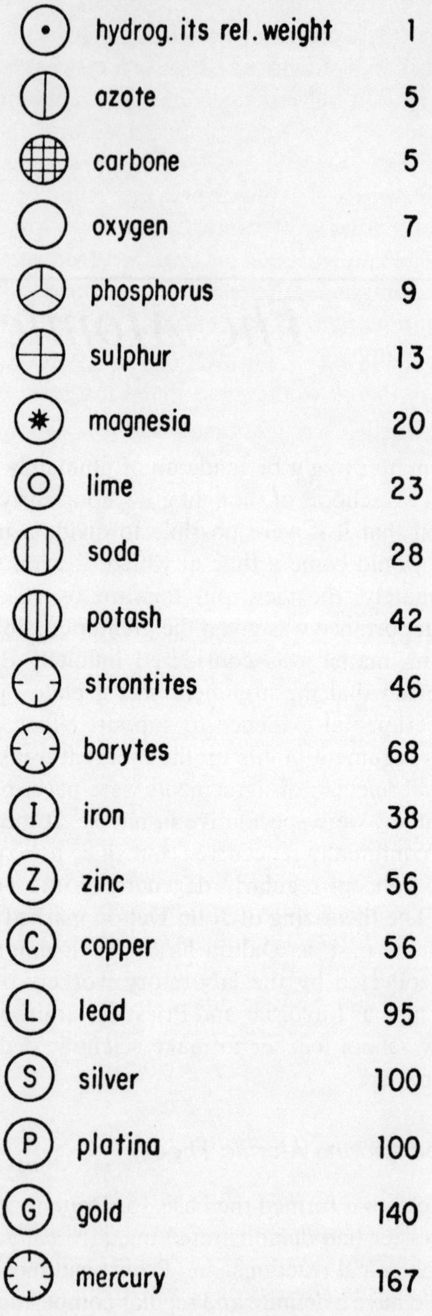

14

Chemistry

⊙	hydrog. its rel. weight	1
⏀	azote	5
⊕	carbone	5
◯	oxygen	7
⊘	phosphorus	9
⊕	sulphur	13
✳	magnesia	20
⊙	lime	23
⏀	soda	28
⦀	potash	42
⊕	strontites	46
⟁	barytes	68
Ⓘ	iron	38
Ⓩ	zinc	56
Ⓒ	copper	56
Ⓛ	lead	95
Ⓢ	silver	100
Ⓟ	platina	100
Ⓖ	gold	140
⊛	mercury	167

Fig. 3-1. **Chemical symbols and atomic weights, 1808. (From Hildebrand and Powell, *Principles of Chemistry*, seventh edition, MacMillan & Co., 1964, p. 34.)**

light of present knowledge the first atomic theory was inadequate, but we must also admit that the exceptions go far beyond the chemical criteria that made possible the original statements. In much of what is done in chemistry today, we act as if Dalton's atoms really exist. It is only in the more esoteric aspects of the science that we concern ourselves with the exceptions to his fundamental statements. On the basis of his predecessors' work, Dalton formulated five statements that described the atom as he conceived it. It must be emphasized that no matter how certain we are today of the existence of atoms, we are still dealing with a *concept;* the direct and immediate perception of an atom is as impossible today as it was one hundred and sixty years ago. We may be more certain of the reality of the atom, but this certainty is gained from indirect supportive data rather than from direct observation.

The first modern theory of the atom made five assumptions:

1. All matter is made up of indivisible and indestructible particles.
2. The atoms of an element are all alike in their physical and chemical properties.
3. The atoms of different elements are unlike in their properties.
4. The atoms of elements join together in some fashion to form the molecules of compounds.
5. Atoms of two or more elements may form more than one compound, but the simplest molecule will be formed by one atom of each of the elements involved.

It is interesting to note that the first four points, those that were based on experimental evidence, are still tenable if considered in context; but the last is not supportable. It is the fifth point which represented Dalton's device for simplicity in the area of chemical combination that did not reflect in any degree the data or facts available to him. This theory was adequate to account for the data available at the time, and although it is now inadequate, it remains a significant step forward in the application of logical deduction to the facts at hand. There is little difficulty in correcting erroneous notions, if hindsight is available. The first modification of the atomic theory became necessary after the collection of certain data by Dalton's contemporary, Gay-Lussac.

3-2 The Law of Combining Volumes

As has been noted previously, the chemists of the 18th and early 19th centuries found it possible to gain considerable insight into the nature of chemical reactions through the study of matter in the gaseous state. As the number of known chemical elements grew, there were more and more instances of direct interactions between gases which could be studied in terms of the volumes of reactants and products. As examples, let us consider the following:

hydrogen	+	chlorine	→	hydrogen chloride
(1 volume)		(1 volume)		(2 volumes)
hydrogen	+	oxygen	→	water
(2 volumes)		(1 volume)		(2 volumes)
nitrogen	+	oxygen	→	nitric acid
(1 volume)		(1 volume)		(2 volumes)

Observations such as these led Gay-Lussac to compose the statement of the *Law of Combining Volumes:* When gases combine chemically, the volumes are found to be expressible in ratios of small whole numbers. Implicit, of course, is the further statement that the temperature and pressure must be the same for each gas in accord with the gas laws elucidated earlier. One difficulty was introduced, however, when the volumes of reactants and products were considered. Dalton could not understand the volume decrease in the formation of water, since his initial premise was that the size of compound atoms (molecules) should be equal to the sum of the sizes of the constituent elementary atoms. Then, too, Gay-Lussac had found it necessary to overlook some of his own data to a degree, since the actual results approached, but did not reach, the simple ratios which he stated in his law. The inherent inaccuracies of physical measurements are now well known, but it must be admitted that in rounding off figures to accomplish agreement with hypothesis, there is always the danger of making incorrect assumptions. However, in this instance the accumulation of data only increased belief in the inherent soundness of the original statement.

3-3 Atoms, Molecules, and Avogadro's Hypothesis

It remained for the Italian physicist Avogadro to bring forward an explanation for the relations found between the volumes of reactants and products. Consider the reaction already given in which hydrogen and chlorine react to form hydrogen chloride. Equal volumes of the gases interact to form a product having a volume equal to the sum of the volumes of the reactants. If we look at the reaction on the atomic and molecular level it is assumed that atoms of hydrogen and chlorine have formed molecules which contain at least one atom each of hydrogen and chlorine. If the gases were monatomic we would have to conclude that the molecules produced were distributed in a volume twice as large as that of one of the reactants. This would mean that the space effectively occupied by one molecule was twice as great as that taken up by one atom; or, to state it another way, a unit volume would contain only one-half as many molecules of hydrogen chloride as atoms of either hydrogen or chlorine. Even though some logical construct could be erected to account for such an explanation, it would become untenable when the reaction of hydrogen and oxygen was considered, since in this reaction the volume changes in a ratio of three to two.

The hypothesis that Avogadro made to account for the variation in the data contained two points. First, he assumed that equal volumes of gases, under the same conditions of temperature and pressure, contained equal numbers of molecules. There was considerable support for this idea from the gas laws because all gases, irrespective of their chemical nature, responded to physical changes in environment in exactly the same fashion. Using this premise as a foundation, the second point in the hypothesis was that elementary particles of gases could contain more than one atom. In this light, the reaction of hydrogen and chlorine can be viewed as the reaction between molecules of hydrogen and chlorine (each molecule being composed of two atoms) to produce molecules of hydrogen chloride. In the chemical symbolism that will be discussed in the next few pages:

$$H_2 + Cl_2 \rightarrow 2HCl$$

The symbols H_2 and Cl_2 have the understood coefficient 1; the coefficient indicates numbers of molecules or volumes of gases that react or are produced in the interaction.

3-4 The Calculation of Atomic Weights

When the weights of the reactants and the products are considered in the light of the laws and hypotheses developed to this point, it becomes possible to establish values for atomic weights. The numbers assigned have no units, because we cannot determine the absolute value for the mass of an atom by the study of chemical reactions. However, granted the correctness of Avogadro's hypothesis, it is easily possible to ascertain the masses of atoms relative to some arbitrarily chosen standard. Several different elements have been chosen as reference weights, but the one most used during the development of the atomic weight scale was oxygen. The choice was based largely on the observation that oxygen formed a great many compounds, so that many reactions were available from which to determine the atomic weights of other elements.

The scale of atomic weights assembled by Dalton had been based on his erroneous postulate that molecules were composed of one atom of each of the reacting elements; hence, on a relative scale the atomic weights of hydrogen and oxygen were one and eight, respectively. The subsequent recognition that a molecule of water had in it two atoms of hydrogen and one of oxygen made a change in this ratio necessary. Because hydrogen was the lightest (least dense) of the gases known, the decision was made to change the atomic weight ratio to one to sixteen for hydrogen and oxygen so as to avoid having a weight less than one. Oxygen was established as the reference standard, and all other atomic weights were expressed in relation to it.

The technological revolution that accompanied the development of science made increasingly accurate measurements possible, and the study of the weights of materials which reacted led to the discovery that atomic weights were not integer values. It was more than one hundred years before atomic and nuclear physicists were able to provide an explanation for these observations, and even now we can still make use of chemically determined atomic weights for the study of chemical reactions.

The determination of atomic weights of gases was initially easier than for other elements. When oxygen was chosen as a standard with an atomic weight of sixteen, it was possible to find the atomic weight of other elemental gases, and also the molecular weights of compounds, by using as a basis the volume occupied by thirty-two grams of oxygen (since oxygen is assumed to have two atoms per molecule). This volume was found to be 22.4 liters at 0°C and a pressure of one atmosphere. The weight of gas occupying this volume is defined as the *gram-molecular weight,* and is the number representing the molecular weight with units of grams attached. The mass of an atom could be determined if it were possible to count the number of molecules present in this volume. There are various methods available now, for counting molecules per volume; the number, termed *Avogadro's number,* is given as 6.012×10^{23}. While we will not make use of this number, nor of the actual mass of the atom, it will be necessary to adopt some method of shorthand notation so that we can state succinctly and unequivocally not only the qualitative changes, but also the quantitative relationships that are characteristic of chemical reactions.

3-5   The Meaning of Chemical Symbols and Equations

The symbol for a chemical element is basically an abbreviation. It is often taken directly from the name of the element—H for hydrogen, O for oxygen, He for helium—or it may be derived from the Latin names assigned in the historical past—Fe for iron, from *ferrum*, is a case in point. However, when these symbols are employed in the construction of a chemical equation, we find that the symbols take on additional meaning. The statement

$$2H_2 + O_2 \rightarrow 2H_2O$$

is more than a description of the formation of water. The composition of the molecules is indicated, and the conservation of matter is shown by the fact that both the right and the left sides have the same number of each type of atom. The equation can be interpreted as indicating that two molecules of hydrogen, each containing two atoms, react with one molecule of oxygen, also a molecule of two atoms to form two molecules, each of which is made up of two atoms of hydrogen and one of oxygen. But a weight relationship is implicit, as well, if we remember that the relative masses of hydrogen and oxygen atoms are one and sixteen. If we look upon the symbol H_2 as representing two grams of hydrogen and O_2 as representing 32 grams of oxygen we can relate the interaction on a weight basis. The chemical equation is a statement that can place the science of chemistry on a quantitative base, and it indicates the existence of order and predictability which is characteristic of the physical sciences.

QUESTIONS FOR STUDY AND REVIEW

1. How many of Dalton's five assumptions were the early Greeks likely to have made in speculating about the nature of matter?

2. In the light of this chapter, does the Law of Definite Proportions indicate whether water's formula should be H_2O? (See Question 5, Chapter 2).

3. What relation does the Law of Combining Volumes bear to the Law of Definite Proportions?

4. The scale upon which the atomic weights are based does not have to be oxygen taken as 16. Why was oxygen chosen? Why oxygen equal to 16? Would hydrogen as 1 do as well?

5. The various chemical symbols used by chemists have a long history. Some follow from the Greek, some from the Latin and some are quite American, indeed. What are the literal and chemical meanings for the following symbols: Na, K, Ag, Am, Bk, Cf, Si, Kr?

Chapter 4

The Kinetic-Molecular Theory

The success of the atomic theory in its applications to chemical reactions led gradually to the development of a still broader conceptual framework which related the ultimate particles of matter to the physical properties of macroscopic particles and to energy relations observable in laboratory experiments. The kinetic-molecular theory is not credited to a single individual, but rather is viewed as being comprised of two fundamental postulates that were applied in a variety of circumstances. These basic assumptions are that all matter is made up of discrete particles (molecules) and that these molecules are in constant motion. In addition, it is necessary to understand that the motion of molecules differs from that of larger objects, because the collisions which take place are of a type which we call *elastic*.

4-1 Elastic Collisions and Brownian Motion

It is easier to describe what is meant by an elastic collision in qualitative terms by establishing what it is *not* than by attacking the problem directly. If a ball is dropped onto a concrete floor, each successive bounce is less high than the one which preceded it; eventually the ball ceases to move and lies on the floor. This change results from a series of inelastic collisions in which the kinetic energy (the energy of motion) of the ball is gradually reduced. The physicist deals easily with this process, and demonstrates that the energy which the ball possessed by virtue of its motion has been converted to heat. Both ball and floor are warmer than they were originally. An elastic collision of ball and floor would not result in the transformation of mechanical energy to heat energy, but the ball would continue to rebound indefinitely to its original height so long as it was not affected by some other agent introduced into the system.

It is possible to make a simple observation which will support the idea that molecules are in motion, and which will supply data supporting the concept of elastic collisions. If we observe with a microscope a small solid particle suspended in a liquid, we see that the particle is not still but follows an erratic path. The velocity appears to be a function of particle size, so that as the mass decreases the velocity increases. The small object seldom travels far; in fact, it appears to tend to move randomly in the vicinity of a particular point in space. This erratic behavior is called *Brownian motion* in recognition of the British botanist who first observed it. Brownian motion provides us with supporting evidence for the assumption that molecules are in motion, since the behavior of the observed particle can be explained if we hypothesize that it is being continually bombarded by rapidly moving molecules which are beyond the resolving power of the microscope. A similar action is found with dust particles suspended in air, and since we have already seen that the study of the physical properties of gases can be carried out more readily than those of liquids and solids, let us re-examine the gas laws in terms of the kinetic theory.

4-2   Boyle's Law and Kinetic Theory

Because gases are compressible over such a wide range, there are two more statements which observation indicates are reasonable concerning the molecules that make up a gas. The first of these is that the distances between the molecules are very large compared with the dimensions of the molecules themselves; the second is that the forces which exist between the molecules are very small. If a gas is confined, the walls of the container are impermeable to the molecules. Any increase in the volume of the container results in an expansion of the contents because the motion of the particles assures their completely random distribution.

If we consider the quantitative statement of Boyle's law, we find that the kinetic-molecular theory gives a very reasonable explanation. If the volume of a gas is reduced by one-half, the pressure becomes twice as great (Fig. 4-1). The motion of the molecules results in more collisions between molecules and container walls. The phenomenon that we call pressure is occasioned by such collisions against the walls. When the volume is made smaller, the number of molecules per unit volume becomes larger, the collisions per

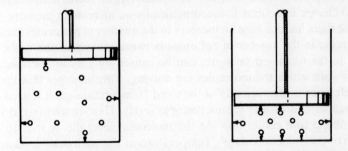

Fig. 4-1.   When the volume is reduced, the increase in the number of molecules in a unit volume causes an increase in pressure.

unit area on the walls increase in frequency and the pressure is increased. Within reasonable limits, Boyle's law is valid, but it is not difficult to see that as the pressure is increased to higher and higher values some modification will be necessary because the distances between molecules will be much smaller. When weak forces do become apparent between the molecules, their freedom of movement is restricted, and the actual space filled by the molecules themselves is then an appreciable fraction of the volume of the container. In fact, very precise measurements make it obvious that Boyle's law is obeyed strictly only by *perfect gases*. A perfect gas is defined as one in which the molecules agree with the assumptions that we made above.

4-3   The Law of Partial Pressures

There is another law which can be explained by a consideration of the assumptions of the kinetic-molecular theory. The *Law of Partial Pressures* states that the total pressure exerted by a mixture of different gases in a container is equal to the sum of the pressures which would be exerted by the component gases if each occupied the same volume by itself. If molecules are very small, and very far apart, then in the absence of any chemical interaction the molecules of different gases would have no more effect on one another than would those of a single gas. This is evident if we consider the mixture of gases which we call air. The overall composition remains approximately the same for dry air, but the percentage of water vapor can change drastically without any obvious alterations in the relative concentrations of the other gases in the mixture.

4-4   Charles' Law and Kinetic Theory

The kinetic-molecular theory provides new insights into Charles' law just as it does for Boyles' law, but an interesting new relationship is indicated between molecular motion and the properties of a sample of a gas. If the temperature of a gas is increased, the volume must be increased if the pressure is to be maintained constant. Alternatively, an increase in temperature with no change in volume is accompanied by an increase in pressure. But in this case there has not been an increase in the number of molecules present, so the increase in the number of collisions between molecules and walls, which results in the increased pressure, can be caused only by an increase in the velocity with which the molecules are moving. This indicates that there is a vast difference in the meaning of the word "temperature" as it is used on the macroscopic and on the submicroscopic levels. Heat is transferred from a hotter object to a cooler one. At the molecular level this is seen to be the transferring of kinetic energy. Temperature at the molecular level is not a meaningful term unless we redefine the concept, and absolute zero—the absence of heat—is marked by the complete cessation of molecular motion.

Of course, it must be noted that at very low temperatures we are not dealing with real gases, let alone perfect gases, because all elements and compounds are liquefied at temperatures at least several degrees above absolute zero. The weak forces between the molecules become significant as the kinetic energy of the molecules drops to a very low level.

4-5   Rate of Diffusion

But what is this property of matter which we called kinetic energy? A study of mechanics gives us the equation

$$\text{Kinetic energy} = \tfrac{1}{2}mv^2.$$

The kinetic energy which any body possesses is a function of its mass and the square of its velocity, and if samples of gases whose molecules have different masses are at the same temperature (the molecules have the same average kinetic energy) then the molecules making up the two samples must have different velocities. This is not a difficult proposition to verify experimentally, because molecules of different velocities will diffuse through air at different rates. The simultaneous introduction of hydrogen chloride and ammonia into opposite ends of a closed tube results in the formation of a white ring of finely divided ammonium chloride according to the reaction

$$HCl + NH_3 \rightarrow NH_4Cl$$

The ring forms in the tube nearer to the point of introduction of the HCl than of the ammonia because the mass of the molecule HCl is greater than that of NH_3.

4-6   Properties of Solids and Liquids

The kinetic-molecular theory provides us with explanations for the properties of liquids and solids as well as of gases. If it did not, the theory would be inadequate and would long since have been superseded by another whose application was all-encompassing. When we consider the state of the molecules in a liquid we can envision them in constant motion but limited in their range. The molecules are in such close proximity one to another that the forces of attraction are appreciable and the molecules are confined to a particular volume. However, we know that liquids do evaporate and this means that individual molecules can escape. Evaporation results in the cooling of the liquid which remains behind, and if temperature is a measure of kinetic energy it is apparent that the molecules remaining have a lower average kinetic energy than did those originally present. It is also reasonable to conclude that all of the molecules present do not have the same energy, else all could escape at once. Instead it seems more proper to talk about an average kinetic energy for all of the molecules in a mass, and to describe those which escape as being the ones with the highest kinetic energies. The loss of the most energetic molecules results in a lowering of the average for those that remain behind.

This explanation is still insufficient because it has not dealt with that property which we call the *heat of vaporization*. When the temperature of a liquid is raised to the boiling point, a continuous application of heat is required to maintain the boiling process, even though the temperature of the vapor formed is no higher than that of the liquid. The temperature has not been increased, and yet energy has been added to the system. This is not a contradiction of the kinetic theory, but rather indicates that the introduction of energy is necessary to overcome the forces which held the molecules in close proximity one to another. Conversely, the condensation of a gas to form a liquid results in an increase in the temperature of the environment. The temperature moderating effect of lakes and oceans can, in part, be attributed to this phenomenon. An increase in temperature which increases the rate of evaporation results in the absorption of energy. The absorption of energy creates a counter force which tends to lower the temperature so that variations in temperature are lessened.

The transformation of a liquid to a solid is susceptible to an explanation similar to that just given for the boiling of a liquid. The molecules which make up a solid are not firmly fixed in position, but rather are oscillating randomly about a point in space. Freedom of motion is sharply limited by the surrounding molecules, and the forces which exist between molecules in solids are stronger than those which exist in liquids. Occasional molecules do escape from a solid surface—mothballs disappear without ever melting—but the rate is relatively low. An increase in temperature will increase the rate of *sublimation* (the direct transformation of a solid to a vapor); more commonly the solid will melt. The energy required to bring about this latter change in state is the *heat of fusion,* and represents the energy required to overcome the attractive forces which hold the molecules in their ordered solid structure.

There are other phenomena which could be discussed in the light of this theory, but let us turn our attention to a consideration of the structure and nomenclature of molecules themselves.

QUESTIONS FOR STUDY AND REVIEW

1. How is it possible to construct a useful theory, such as the kinetic theory, if the postulates upon which it is based cannot be proved?

2. A heat pump is a device that cools by transferring heat energy from one object to a second one. Would it be possible to attain a temperature of absolute zero in this fashion?

3. Anyone who has ever inflated a bicycle tire knows that the pump gets hotter as the pumping continues. How can this observation be explained by the kinetic theory?

4. Samples of HCl and NH₃ are introduced into a tube one meter long. The gases are at the same temperature, so the kinetic energies of the molecules are equal. Accordingly, we can write the equations

$$KE_{HCl} = KE_{NH_3} \quad \text{and} \quad \tfrac{1}{2}mv^2 \text{ (HCl)} = \tfrac{1}{2}mv^2 \text{ (NH}_3\text{)}.$$

If the mass of the HCl is approximated as 36, and that of the NH₃ as 16, how far will each travel before they meet and react? (*Hint:* Since we do not know the velocities we cannot tell how long this will take, but the distances traveled in any period of time will be proportional to the velocities.)

5. How can we explain the observation that daily temperature variations in the desert are so much greater than those in a tropical rain forest?

6. Why is the diffusion of dissolved molecules in water so much slower than the diffusion of the same molecules through air?

Chapter 5

Nomenclature and Classification

As chemistry developed as a theoretical science in the early 19th century, it became increasingly apparent that for practical and pragmatic reasons there must evolve a systematic nomenclature and symbolism to express the relations that were being observed in chemical reactions. The alchemists of the Middle Ages had used symbols to denote the qualitative changes that they observed, and also to identify the limited number of substances with which they dealt, but the mysticism involved with their activities led them to be deliberately obscure. Dalton had taken over some of their symbols and had adapted them to his revolutionary ideas of atoms and molecules, but his devices soon proved to be inadequate. In the past two chapters we have anticipated the system which was adopted, largely because of the influence of Berzelius, in the years following the acceptance of the atomic theory. Abbreviations were used for the names of the elements. The symbols thus chosen really stood for atoms, and molecular formulas were constructed from the chemical symbols for the atoms. In addition, halting steps were made in the direction of the classification of the elements according to their physical properties.

Of more significance, perhaps, was the growth of the system of the naming of compounds which has survived to the present day. The chemical symbols of the elements were well adapted for written communication, but they were not sufficient for verbal usage. Since the transmission of information by speech required generally-agreed-upon definitions of words, there grew up a specialized vocabulary within the community of chemists. To begin with, the elements were categorized as metals or nonmetals on the basis of their physical and chemical properties. Actually, a set of criteria was chosen to describe the metals, and any element that failed to fit was automatically a nonmetal. The metals were those elements that were conductors of heat and electricity and were lustrous in appearance. Their typical chemical property was that they combined more or less readily with oxygen to give a compound that had alkaline properties when dissolved in water. The nonmetals possessed none of these qualities, and their compounds with oxygen gave acids in aqueous solution.

5-1 The Naming of Chemical Compounds

It was well known that metals and nonmetals reacted with each other to form compounds, and since there were so many of these compounds, it soon became necessary to impose some order on the list. Trivial names were not enough because they did not reflect either the elemental composition or the number of atoms of each type included in the molecule. The simplest compounds were those which are made up of only two types of atoms. The naming of these entailed the identification of the elements involved and, in addition, required some change in the names of the elements to indicate that a compound was being named. Accepted practice called for the use of the name of the metal without modification, and the name of the nonmetal was altered by use of the suffix *-ide*. Thus, the compound formed by the combination of sodium and chlorine was sodium chloride, while that containing magnesium and oxygen was magnesium oxide. When two nonmetals combined to form a compound, an arbitrary classification was adopted which stated that one element was more nonmetallic than the other so that the system could be preserved. Carbon dioxide is an example.

If two elements could form no more than one compound, then there would have been little difficulty. However, it was found necessary to name as many as five different compounds, all of which are made up of only two types of atoms. We can indicate the manner in which this task was carried out by considering the various molecules containing only nitrogen and oxygen.

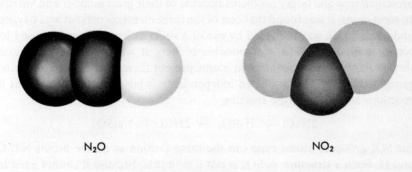

N₂O   NO₂

Fig. 5-1. Models of the molecules of two of the oxides of nitrogen.

N_2O	nitrous oxide
NO	nitric oxide
N_2O_3	nitrogen trioxide
NO_2	nitrogen dioxide
N_2O_5	nitrogen pentoxide

The use of the prefixes *di-*, *tri-*, and *pent-* is easy to understand. In each instance we are indicating the number of atoms of a particular type that is present in the molecule. The suffixes *-ic* and *-ous* are equally specific but less obvious. The choice here is not arbitrary but is based on the relative chemical combining power of the atom in question in a particular compound. Just as oxygen was chosen as an arbitrary standard in establishing the atomic weight scale, so hydrogen and chlorine were selected as reference elements in determining relative combining powers. Hydrogen and chlorine form hydrogen chloride, a compound whose molecules are made up of one atom of each element. An atom that combined with or replaced one atom of hydrogen or chlorine was described as having a combining power of one. Water, with a molecular formula H_2O, contained oxygen with a combining power of two. It was not long before the concept *valence* was introduced, and with it the depiction of hydrogen as $+1$ and chlorine as -1 in their combined forms, while oxygen, except in a small group of peroxides, had an invariant valence of -2.

As has been shown above, it is possible to use prefixes to indicate differences in molecular structure; but there is another system by which the valence state of an element is denoted when it is referred to the standard. Oxygen has a combining power of two, but it forms compounds with nitrogen in which the molecular formulas are N_2O and NO. The assumption was made, and found valid much later on the basis of atomic structure, that nitrogen was the element with the variable valence. The suffixes *-ous* and *-ic* were chosen to indicate the lower and higher states, respectively, and numerous pairs such as cuprous-cupric and ferrous-ferric were named.

Compounds whose molecules contained three different types of atoms presented new and larger problems because of their great number and variety. In most cases, it was found that one of the three elements present was oxygen, and its presence was indicated by use of a suffix different from that used for binary compounds. This was possible because it was recognized that even though there were three different atoms present there were only two reactive groups. One type of atom acted independently while the others took part in reactions as a unit. In the reaction

$$2NaCl + H_2SO_4 \rightarrow 2HCl + Na_2SO_4$$

the SO_4 group of atoms reacts in the same fashion as do the atoms Na, Cl and H. Such a structure as SO_4 is not a molecule, because it cannot exist by itself but is found only within the framework of molecules. These collections of atoms were termed *radicals* (see Table 5-1). The names assigned had to

Table 5-1   The Formulas, Valences, and Names of some Typical Inorganic Chemical Radicals

Formula	Valence	Name
CO_3	-2	carbonate
ClO_3	-1	chlorate
SO_3	-2	sulfite
SO_4	-2	sulfate
OH	-1	hydroxide
PO_4	-3	phosphate
CrO_4	-2	chromate
AsO_3	-1	arsenate
NO_2	-1	nitrite
NO_3	-1	nitrate
NH_4	$+1$	ammonium

specify both the elements present and the relative combining power of the radical, since it was found that more than one radical could be formed from the same two elements. Consider the list of compounds in Table 5-2. The use of the stem *chlor-* indicates the presence of chlorine, while the *-ite* and *-ate* show that oxygen is also included. The suffixes also denote the relative combining power or valence of the chlorine as measured by the number of oxygen atoms in the radical. The fact that, in this case, there are more than two compounds leads to the use of the two prefixes *hypo-* and *per-* (oxygen). Hypo means less than and hyper (or per) means more than. With these few terms, it is possible to name the vast majority of compounds.

Table 5-2

$NaClO$	sodium hypochlorite
$NaClO_2$	sodium chlorite
$NaClO_3$	sodium chlorate
$NaClO_4$	sodium perchlorate

Two other groups are of sufficient importance to mention here, but we need not consider some of the minor ramifications found necessary in special cases. We noted earlier in this chapter that compounds of metals with oxygen (the metallic oxides) produce an alkaline or basic reaction when dissolved in water, while the oxides of nonmetals give an acidic reaction. Simple working definitions of base and acid, sufficient for our purposes, can be given in terms of the presence within the molecule of an atom or a particular radical. An *acid* is a compound that contains hydrogen, and a *base* is one that contains the hydroxyl radical, OH. The reaction of an acid with a base results in the formation of a salt and water:

$$HNO_3 + NaOH \rightarrow NaNO_3 + H_2O$$

Water is looked upon as being made up of one atom of hydrogen and one hydroxyl radical, and could best be signified by the formula HOH. A *salt* is defined as that type of molecule produced by the reaction of an acid and a base. The name usually applied to the compound whose molecular formula is H_2SO_4 is sulfuric acid, but it could more properly be called hydrogen sulfate. It is possible to replace only one of the hydrogen atoms in salt formation, the molecule produced having a formula $NaHSO_4$, sodium hydrogen sulfate. This compound is both a salt and an acid because the second hydrogen can also be replaced by an atom of a metal.

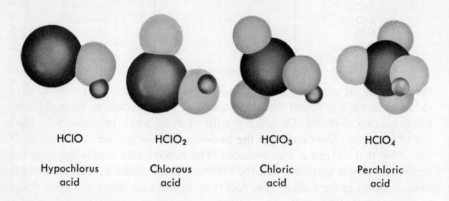

HClO	HClO$_2$	HClO$_3$	HClO$_4$
Hypochlorus acid	Chlorous acid	Chloric acid	Perchloric acid

Fig. 5-2. **Molecular models of the oxyacids of chlorine that correspond to the salts in Table 5-2.**

A better known example of a radical that contains three atoms, one of which is hydrogen, is HCO_3. This group might be called a hydrogen carbonate, but is more commonly known as bicarbonate. The prefix *bi-* indicates the presence of hydrogen. Sulfuric acid is formed through the reaction of sulfur trioxide (SO_3) with water. But not all acids are produced in such a fashion, because hydrochloric acid is a solution of hydrogen chloride (HCl) in water. The formation of a base can be typified by a consideration of the reaction of sodium oxide (Na_2O) with water:

$$Na_2O + H_2O \rightarrow 2NaOH$$

5-2 The Periodic Law and the Periodic Table

The study of the formulas of compounds and detailed consideration of the chemical and physical properties of elements and compounds led to interesting discoveries of similarities of properties. Two groups of elements were known to have chemical and physical properties which, although not identical, formed a regular gradation. Lithium, sodium, and potassium (the alkali metals), all with low densities and high reactivities, and fluorine, chlorine, bromine, and iodine (the halogens), nonmetals with similar chemical prop-

	I	II	III	IV	V	VI	VII	VIII
	Li=7	Be=9,4	B=11	C=12	N=14	O=16	F=19	
1	Na=23	Mg=24	Al=27,3	Si=28	P=31	S=32	Cl=35,5	
2	K=39	Ca=40	=44	Ti=50	V=51	Cr=52	Mn=55	Fe=56 Co=58 Ni=59 Cu=63
3	(Cu)	Zn=65	=68	=72	As=75	Se=78	Br=80	
4	Rb=85	Sr=87	Yt=92	Zr=90	Nb=94	Mo=96	=99	Ru=104 Rh=104 Pl=106 Ag=108
5	(Ag)	Cd=112	In=113	Sn=118	Sb=122	Te=125	J=127	
6	Cs=133	Ba=137	La	Ce=138	—	—	—	—
7	—	—	—	—	—	—	—	—
8	—	—	Er	Di	Ta=182	W=184	—	Os=199 Ir=197 Pt=197 Au=197
9	(Au)	Hg=200	Tl=204	Pb=207	Bi=208	—	—	—
10	—	—	—	Th=231	—	Ur=240	—	—

(After « к снстеме элементов » of 1870. The numbers are the atomic weights as Mendeleev knew them.)

Fig. 5-3. One of Mendeleev's earliest periodic tables. (From Hildebrand and Powell, Principles of Chemistry, seventh edition. MacMillan & Co., 1964, p. 22.)

erties, first served to point up the possibility of classification. Of course, the climate of scientific opinion was receptive to attempts to find order in the area of chemical elements. For two hundred years men had been trying to find order in the universe (or impose order upon it), and the Russian chemist Mendeleev was now to do for chemistry what had already been done in many areas of biology and physics. Some attempts had already been made, but his effort was the first to be carried to fruition. The *periodic table* depicted inside the front cover is a refinement of that of Mendeleev (Fig. 5-3), but is founded on his original theses.

It must be recognized, of course, that the work of a great many chemists contributed to the success of this effort, for the first twenty or so elements had been discovered and their properties catalogued. The gradation of properties in the two groups already mentioned provided the starting point. If we list the first seven elements then known (ignoring hydrogen, the lightest) in order of increasing atomic weight, we note a gradual change from the metallic properties of lithium to the nonmetallic characteristics of fluorine. The next element then known in order of increasing atomic weight was sodium, and it seemed logical to locate it in a common group with lithium. When the sequence was completed, it was found that chlorine ended in the column with fluorine and that the third series would then begin with potassium, an element very similar to those directly above it. Most significantly, the properties of each element were found to relate more closely to those directly above or below than to the ones located on either side. Mendeleev stated his *Law of Periodicity* as a starting point for the construction of the periodic table. The law stated that the properties of the elements, as well as the properties of their compounds, form a periodic function of the atomic weights of the elements. Although it will not serve our purpose here to discuss at any great length the historical development of the periodic table, let us look briefly at the evidence that led to the periodic law. The tabulation lists certain typical compounds for the first fourteen elements, then known, after hydrogen.

Lithium	*Beryllium*	*Boron*	*Carbon*	*Nitrogen*	*Oxygen*	*Fluorine*
LiCl	$BeCl_2$	BCl_3	CCl_4			
			CH_4	NH_3	OH_2	FH
Li_2O	BeO	B_2O_3	CO_2	N_2O_5		

Sodium	*Magnesium*	*Aluminum*	*Silicon*	*Phosphorus*	*Sulfur*	*Chlorine*
NaCl	$MgCl_2$	$AlCl_3$	$SiCl_4$	PCl_5		
			SiH_4	PH_3	SH_2	ClH
Na_2O	MgO	Al_2O_3	SiO_2	P_2O_5	SO_3	

As we delve more deeply into the structure of the atom, we will find additional evidence which will help to explain the periodic law. Some seeming anomalies that appear farther along in the periodic table will be elucidated, but the fundamental similarities that gave rise to it will only be supported.

The next great advances that took place resulted from the discovery that Dalton's atomic theory stood in need of modification, and that the chemical properties of the atoms of the elements were determined by the interior arrangements within the atoms of particles of still smaller dimensions.

QUESTIONS FOR STUDY AND REVIEW

1. What are the names and molecular weights of the following compounds?

$AgBr$	$NaBrO_3$
$Al_2(SO_4)_3$	BaO
CaF_2	KOH
K_2CrO_4	$(NH_4)_2CO_3$
KNO_3	$MgNH_4PO_4$
SO_2	HCl

2. When we calculate valences, we usually assume that oxygen has a valence of -2. Using this assumption and the information in Table 5-1, what are the valences of each of the atoms in the compounds listed in Question 1? For which compounds is the information given insufficient?

Chapter 6

A New Atomic Theory

The story of the discovery of the inner structure of the atom is one of the most fascinating in the history of science, but since it involves primarily the activities of physicists, we will not concern ourselves with studying it in detail here. However, the modifications made necessary in Dalton's atomic theory should be mentioned since these are of primary importance in our present understanding of the relation of atomic structure to the manner in which atoms interact chemically. Let us consider the points one by one and, in this fashion, discover the basis for the atom described by Niels Bohr in the early years of this century.

6-1   The Structure of the Atom

One of the earliest indications that atoms might be capable of modification came with the discovery that solutions could conduct electricity, and that the particles involved in the conduction were apparently atoms which had in some manner acquired an electrical charge. These electrically charged atoms were termed *ions*. Certain of these particles had negative charges, while others displayed a positive charge. The experimental verification of the existence of the electron and the demonstration of the relation of electrical charge to combining power gave rise to a concept of the atom with an internal structure. Each atom was envisioned as being made up of a quantity of matter that possessed a positive electrical charge, together with a number of electrons of negative charge sufficient to balance exactly the positive charge. Such an atom was analogous to a plum pudding with electrons for raisins. When a chemical reaction took place between two atoms, there was an interchange of electrons, although no hypothesis could suggest a reason for the transfer. The untenability of this model was shown by Rutherford when he demonstrated that the mass of the atom was concentrated in a very small nucleus which was positively charged, while the electrons were relatively far from the nucleus itself. Subsequent to this were the discoveries that the atoms of certain elements were not indivisible, but instead underwent disintegrations that resulted in changes in both the charge and the mass of the nucleus. More than that, it was found that atoms of the same element sometimes had different atomic weights, even though the physical and chemical properties of the element were almost identical. These atoms of the same element which differed only in their masses were called *isotopes*.

6-2   Niels Bohr and the Hydrogen Atom

All of this evidence was incorporated into a new concept of the atom by Niels Bohr. His model of the atom had a central nucleus about which the electrons traveled in much the same fashion as do the planets around the sun, or satellites around the earth. Those electrons farthest from the nucleus possessed the greatest energy and, so, could be most easily removed. The orbit in which the planetary electron moved was determined by the energy that the electron possessed. There was one major difference between the satellite electrons and satellites of the sun or earth. If a satellite orbiting the earth has its energy increased or decreased by some amount, it will assume a new orbit, and the number of such possible orbits is infinite. The orbiting electron was, to the contrary, limited to only a few possible orbits. A discrete and calculable quantity of energy was required to move the electron from one orbit to another, and the introduction of a lesser quantity produced no alteration whatsoever.

The simplest atom, and the one which Bohr found he could describe most exactly by mathematical equations, was that of hydrogen. The nucleus of the hydrogen atom had a single positive charge, and external to the nucleus was a single electron. When energy was added to the electron it assumed a new orbit, and the introduction of enough energy removed the electron from the atom completely. This nucleus was a *proton,* a particle with a mass essentially the same as that of the hydrogen atom. The mass of the electron was found to be only a little more than 1/2000 that of the proton. Chemical interactions of hydrogen with other elements involved only the electron; the integrity of the atom was resident in the nucleus.

6-3   The Nuclear Atom—Bohr's Theory Extended

The next heavier atom on the atomic weight scale was helium, an element distinguished by its failure, so far as was known, to enter into any sort of chemical reaction. Apparently there was some inherent stability in this atom so that it possessed no tendency either to gain or to lose electrons. The nucleus of this atom has a charge of $+2$, while the atomic weight is about 4. Because the atom is electrically neutral, it must have two orbiting electrons, and due to its chemical inertness, it was described as having a complete electron shell. The nucleus was assumed to be made up of four protons and two electrons. Such a combination accounted for both the charge and the mass of the nucleus. (We know now that electrons are not present in the nucleus, but that the nucleus is made up of protons and *neutrons*. The neutron is a particle with a mass very close to that of the proton but with no electrical charge.) The next element in order of increasing atomic weight was lithium. The charge of $+3$ on the nucleus indicated the presence of three orbiting electrons, and the ease with which the lithium atom entered into chemical reactions indicated an inherent tendency in the atom to acquire the stable configuration of helium. The valence of lithium was $+1$; that is, the stable lithium ion had that electrical charge, since it had lost one electron in the process of reacting chemically.

6-4 Atomic Structure and the Periodic Table

The increasing charge on the nucleus with increasing atomic weight gave new sense to the previously constructed periodic table and to the similarities in chemical properties of elements with widely varying atomic weights. Instead of listing the elements in order of increasing atomic weight, let us put them down according to a new definition, *atomic number*. We will define the atomic number of an element as the number of positive electrical charges on the nucleus, and, of course, the number of external electrons in the neutral atom is numerically equal to the nuclear charge. The first period of the table, together with a representation of the electron shells, will give a series of models that can help to relate atomic properties to atomic structure. The charge and not the mass of the nucleus is indicated, because we know that isotopes (atoms with different atomic masses but with the same atomic number) have almost the same chemical properties.

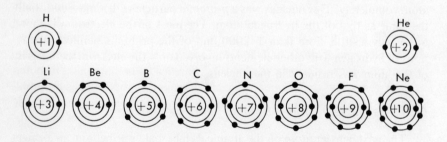

Neon, like helium, is marked by its failure to enter into chemical reactions; hence it also apparently possesses an inherent structural stability. (Recent investigations have shown that certain of the inert gases can form a limited number of chemical compounds; for example, neon and helium may be found capable of chemical interaction. It still appears, however, as if there is an unusual stability in the electron octet.) Lithium, the most metallic of the elements depicted above, reacts violently with fluorine, the most nonmetallic. In the course of the reaction, each atom is altered so that it becomes an ion with the configuration of one of the inert gases. And, it should be noted, these ions are caused to interact only with the greatest difficulty. The ions Li^+ and F^- are exceedingly unreactive, which lends credence to our supposition that there are stable configurational shells within the various atoms. The manner of interaction of some of those elements in this first period will require further discussion, but first let us consider the elements that appear directly below Li and F in the second period.

The chemical properties of sodium and chlorine are very similar to those of lithium and fluorine. If we continue to add electrons to the atom as the atomic number increases, the shell models of the atoms can be seen to be similar in one regard. Both Li and Na have an outer shell containing only one

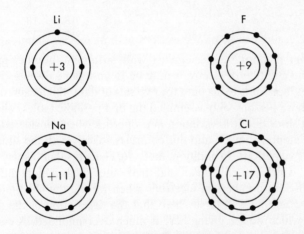

electron, and the loss of this outer electron, in either case, will leave an ion with an inert gas configuration. The gases F and Cl, on the other hand, each require the addition of one electron to complete the outer shell. It *seems* safe to conclude, from these observations, that chemical interactions involve only the electrons in the outer shell, and that the formation of an ion is the result of the atom's attaining an electronic configuration that makes its outer shell complete. The *valence* of an element may now be redefined as the number of electrons gained or lost in the process of chemical interaction, although this definition will need modification when we speak of that type of molecule which is not ionic in character.

6-5   The Long Periods in the Periodic Table

A glance at the periodic table will show that all of the periods do not contain eight elements. If we count hydrogen and helium as the first period, the numbers of elements included in each is as follows: 2, 8, 8, 18, 18, 32. There are a few naturally occurring elements in the seventh period, and all of those atoms synthesized by nuclear physicists are also in the seventh period.

This does not mean that the outer shells contain the number of electrons equal to the number of elements in the long periods. Our knowledge of atomic structure indicates that the outer shell never contains more than eight electrons, but that as the atoms increase in size, certain of the inner shells can have a number of electrons greater than eight. The electron arrangements of the inert gases that mark the ends of the succeeding periods show the configuration when all of the shells are completely filled.

Name	Symbol	Atomic Number	1st	2nd	3rd	4th	5th	6th
Helium	He	2	2					
Neon	Ne	10	2	8				
Argon	A	18	2	8	8			
Krypton	Kr	36	2	8	18	8		
Xenon	Xe	54	2	8	18	18	8	
Radon	Rd	86	2	8	18	32	18	8

The fact that for those elements with an atomic number greater than eighteen the addition of electrons may be in an inner as well as in the outer shell makes it possible to account for two sets of data which caused some difficulty for those persons who assembled the first periodic tables. There are elements that show but little variation in properties when considered in order of increasing atomic number, and this contrasts sharply with the situation noted in the first two periods. In addition, there are elements that display differences in valence, which can only mean that their outer shells may at different times contain different numbers of electrons when we use the shell model for the atom. (It would be well to say here that the description of the structure of the atoms which we are giving here is much oversimplified. A consideration of this subject in greater depth can be found in any number of textbooks, but the model developed here will be satisfactory for the reactions that will be considered as we pursue our study in this volume.)

As an example of both of the seemingly anamolous circumstances just mentioned, let us consider the triplet of elements iron, cobalt, and nickel.

Name	Symbol	At. No.	1st	2nd	3rd	4th
Iron	Fe	26	2	8	14	2
Cobalt	Co	27	2	8	15	2
Nickel	Ni	28	2	8	16	2

It can be seen that electrons are not added to the outermost shell; rather, the increase takes place in the next to last shell. The two valence states of iron, and of cobalt and nickel as well, must result from the loss of an electron from the next outermost shell. If we consider elements still higher in the periodic table, we can find instances in which the added electrons are introduced into the third shell counting from the valence shell. As might be expected, these elements display chemical properties which are so similar that their separation is accomplished only with great difficulty. But now let us step back and consider the manner in which this shell model of the atom can help to clarify our observations of chemical interactions between atoms.

QUESTIONS FOR STUDY AND REVIEW

1. Concentration of the isotope of uranium that is used to make atomic weapons is accomplished by a diffusion process using the gaseous compound UF_6. Explain.

2. From the data given below calculate the valence of each atom and the number of neutrons in the nucleus.

Element	Atomic Number	Atomic Weight
Ca	20	40
Ra	88	226
Fr	87	223
At	85	210
I	53	127

3. The electrons in the shells closer to the nucleus are removed less easily than are those which are farther away. From this statement what conclusion can be drawn concerning the relative reactivities of the metals Cs and K, and the nonmetals I and Cl?

4. The electronic configuration of element number 102 is 2, 8, 18, 32, 32, 8, 2. What would be the atomic number of the inert gas which would be in the same period that includes element 102?

Chapter 7

Chemical Bonding

Chemical reactions between atoms involve only the electrons in the outer shells, but the nature of the chemical bonding is not always the same. In the last chapter, we presented only one of the three common types. The transfer of electrons from one atom to another, which results in the formation of ions with charges opposite in sign and equal in magnitude, is termed *electrovalent* or *ionic bonding*. Actual molecules are never formed, but instead there exist pairs of ions. There is no identification of particular ions with each other, but a unit volume of matter in the liquid or solid state contains enough of each type so that the net electrical charge is zero. This situation is assured because of the strong electrical forces of attraction existing between ions of opposite charge.

7-1 Bonds with Shared Electrons

Two other common types of bonds result from the interaction of atoms, both of which place the atoms in a specific spatial relationship with one another. Instead of a transfer of electrons taking place to form a stable outer electron shell, there is a sharing of electrons between two atoms so that each pair achieves stability. Such a bond, in which the two atoms involved each supply one of the two electrons shared, is termed a *covalent* bond. Perhaps the simplest illustration of a covalent bond is that which exists between the two atoms in a molecule of gas. As noted previously, chlorine gas occurs in this fashion, and our new theory of atomic structure provides an explanation.

Each chlorine atom has seven electrons in its outer shell, but eight are required to produce a stable configuration. When chlorine combines chemically, this condition is achieved by the transfer of an electron from another atom with the formation of a chloride ion. In the elemental state this is not possible, but instead a stable molecule is produced by a mutual sharing of

40

electrons. If we use distinctive symbols for the electrons of two different atoms, we can illustrate the condition which exists:

$$\overset{x\ x}{\underset{x\ x}{\overset{x}{\underset{x}{}}\ Cl\ \overset{\bullet}{\underset{\bullet}{}}\ }} \overset{\bullet\ \bullet}{\underset{\bullet\ \bullet}{}} Cl \overset{\bullet}{\underset{\bullet}{}}$$

Although the two electrons that appear between the two atoms have become common property, they still serve to fill the outer shell of each.

Covalent bonds are also formed when unlike atoms combine chemically, and certain elements almost never combine in any other fashion. Carbon, which has four electrons in its outer shell, does not form either positive or negative ions by itself; instead, it forms covalent bonds, and, most importantly, carbon atoms can link to other carbon atoms to form chains of great length. There are also circumstances in which the number of electrons shared in a covalent bond is four or six. The number is always an even one, for each atom must supply one-half of the electrons in the bond. A variation of the colavent bond is the *coordinate* or *coordinate-covalent* bond; this bond differs in that both of the electrons shared are supplied by one of the participating atoms.

7-2   Radicals—Structure and Charge

In a previous chapter, reference was made to groups of atoms that act as single units in chemical reactions, and the term *radical* was applied to them. These radicals do possess an electrical charge and, therefore, are ionic in nature; yet the bonds that hold them together are covalent and coordinate. Before attempting to indicate the structure of a radical, let us adopt a new symbolism, which we will use from this point on, to represent covalent and coordinate bonds. A covalent bond, with two electrons shared between atoms, will be indicated by a dash: C—C. Multiple bonds will be shown by increasing the number of dashes appropriately. A coordinate bond will be designated by an arrow, and the direction of the arrow will be away from the donor atom: N → O. With this in mind consider the structures of the sulfate and ammonium radicals.

The formula of the sulfate group is SO_4, and its charge is minus two. That is, it has two more electrons than those which would be possessed by the sulfur and oxygen atoms in the elemental state. The common convention for this radical is SO_4^{-2}. Each of the oxygen atoms, and the sulfur atom as well, has six electrons in the outer shell. The structure of this radical involves the formation of two covalent and two coordinate bonds, but also requires that two electrons be supplied to complete the octet shells surrounding each atom.

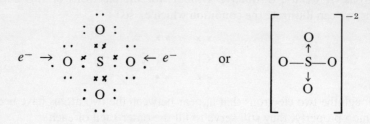

It must be noted that the charge of the radical is not assigned to any particular atom in the radical but, rather, is considered to apply to the entire group of atoms.

Of course, the electrons added must come from some other atom or radical, and so there is associated one or more ions whose total charge is equal and opposite to that of the sulfate ion. The ammonium ion, NH_4^+, which has a positive charge (or valence), could be present. In this case the formula of the compound would be $(NH_4)_2SO_4$. The ammonium ion is formed from a nitrogen atom with five electrons and four hydrogen atoms, each of the latter having had one electron in the atomic state. This is not accomplished by direct combination, but rather by the formation of ammonia, NH_3, and the subsequent addition of a hydrogen ion, which is a hydrogen atom from

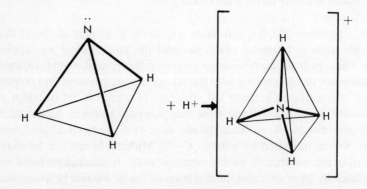

Fig. 7-1. **The three-dimensional representation of the formation of the ammonium ion from ammonia and a proton.**

which the sole electron has been removed. Nitrogen, with five electrons, reacts with three atoms of hydrogen to form the molecule of ammonia. This molecule has a pair of unshared electrons, and the hydrogen ion is added by coordinate covalence at this point. It is interesting to note that once the NH_4^+ ion is formed, the last hydrogen added loses its unique character, so that in this ion all of the hydrogen atoms have the same characteristics and properties. The same can be considered about the sulfate radical. Even though the electron configuration makes it clear that the bonding to two of the oxygen atoms differs from that of the others, we are not able to distinguish among the four. In certain organic molecules, which we will consider later, a clearer division is possible because the molecule does not possess the symmetry of the ions we have considered here.

$$\begin{matrix} & H \\ & | \\ H-N-H \\ & .. \end{matrix} \quad + \quad H^+ \quad \rightarrow \quad \left[\begin{matrix} & H \\ & | \\ H-N-H \\ & | \\ & H \end{matrix}\right]^+$$

Even though the ammonium and sulfate radicals are made up of atoms held together by covalent and coordinate bonds, the bond which exists between the two ions is an electrovalent one. Solid ammonium sulfate is a latticework of independent ions, and in a solution, although the ions are free to move, there is never an excess of one over the other.

The discussion so far has classified bonds into two types, but there are continuous variations within the class of covalent bonds, as we have seen with the coordinate covalent structures. Before we can discuss these, and before we can consider some of the more interesting properties of ions, it will be necessary to define and categorize that special type of mixture which we call a solution.

7-3 Water—A Polar Molecule

A *solution* has previously been defined as a special type of mixture distinguished by the fact that it is homogeneous, and the terms solvent and solute were applied to the components of a solution. Since water is the most common solvent for ionic compounds, we cannot really understand what exists or what reacts in an aqueous solution unless we are familiar with the properties of water.

A molecule of water is composed of two atoms of hydrogen and one of oxygen held together by covalent bonds. Our conventional representation of the water molecule, H_2O, is unfortunate because it fails to point out the fact that this molecule is not symmetrical, and the asymmetry gives to the molecule certain important properties. The orientation of the atoms actually is

$$\begin{matrix} H \quad H \\ \diagdown \diagup \\ O \end{matrix}$$

and the angle formed by the two covalent bonds is about $105°$ (Fig. 7-2). If we go farther in our sketch and indicate the electrons in the outer shell of oxygen, we see that the distribution of electrons is uneven. This means that even though the molecular entity is electrically neutral there is an unequal distribution of electrical charges within. We can see this if we remember that the two hydrogen atoms indicated are actually nuclei with a unit positive

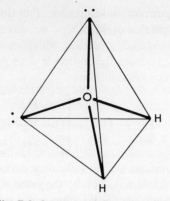

Fig. 7-2. Structure of the water molecule.

charge, and that both exist in the same hemisphere of the molecule. It is possible to show this distribution relatively simply:

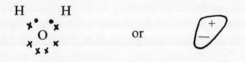

The separation of charges indicated is relative and not absolute. What is being indicated is just that one portion of the molecule is more positive than the other. Any molecule which displays such an electrical asymmetry is called a *polar molecule*. We will see later that certain covalent bonds and covalent molecules are nonpolar, and that these have different properties. In addition, in certain covalent bonds the electrons are not centrally located between the two atoms involved, but are more closely attached to one atom than to the other. The result is that this bond is relatively weak so that one atom can be removed as a positive ion, leaving the remainder of the molecule with an extra electron and a negative charge.

The formation of coordinate bonds has already been indicated, but so far we have considered only the addition of atoms in such bonds. In water, however, a disproportionation can and does take place in which a hydrogen nucleus is transferred from one water molecule to another:

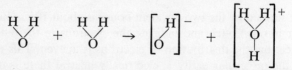

By virtue of their polar nature, water molecules are also attracted to each other, and liquid water is actually composed of aggregates of molecules held together loosely by the electrostatic attraction of the positive end of one molecule for the negative pole of another.

7-4   Ions in Solution

The polar nature of the water molecule accounts for its properties as a solvent. When a compound made up of ions is dissolved in water, each ion, whether positively or negatively charged, is surrounded by a blanket of water molecules all oriented in a manner determined by the charge on the ion (Fig. 7-3). Different compounds have different solubilities, of course, and there are many ionic materials which are only very slightly soluble. It is beyond the scope of this discussion to deal with such phenomena, but it can be noted that water is a good solvent for ions and polar molecules, and it is a poor solvent for nonpolar molecules. The significance of this will be considered when we take up the subject of organic chemistry in a later chapter.

Compounds whose solutions in water are made up in whole or in part of ions are called *electrolytes,* while those which are not ionized are *nonelectrolytes.* The use of these terms originated from the observation that certain solutions were good conductors of electricity while others were not. An electric current traveling through a wire is a stream of electrons flowing along the crystal lattice of the metal atoms. Such a process cannot occur in a solution, but instead the passage of the electric current takes place by the movement of ions through the solution. The excess of electrons at one electrode then are commonly added to a positive ion to give a neutral atom, while at the

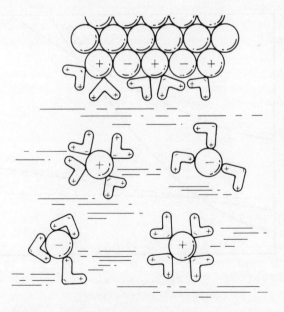

Fig. 7-3.   Hydration of ions in aqueous medium. (From Brown, *General Chemistry,* Charles E. Merrill Books, Inc., 1963, p. 162.)

same time a negative ion is being transformed into an atom at the other electrode by the loss of an electron. If there are no ions in the solution, there can be no current flow. As is so often the case, any classification scheme is an oversimplification, and all electrolytes are not the same. Compounds which are completely ionic are stronger electrolytes—that is, they pass a current more readily—than are those which are composed partly of ions and partly of electrically neutral molecules.

It should be apparent from the foregoing discussion that ions in solution actually act independently of one another, and the only requirement is that the total solution include an equal number of positive and negative charges. If a compound such as sodium chloride is dissolved in water, it is a simple process to evaporate the water and recover the solid compound. We can pretend in such a system that the sodium chloride continued to exist while it was in solution. But what if both sodium nitrate and potassium chloride are added to the same portion of water? It would be incorrect, or at least ill-advised, to state that either of the original materials still exists. The true condition of the solution would be described if we stated that we now had a volume of water containing a certain number of sodium, potassium, chloride and nitrate ions. This can be demonstrated readily if a solution is prepared by dissolving equal quantities of the two salts in a quantity of water, dividing the solution into two parts and evaporating one portion at $100°C$ and the other at $10°C$. The four ions present could form four different compounds: $NaNO_3$, $NaCl$, KNO_3, KCl. From the solubility data given in Fig. 7-4 it

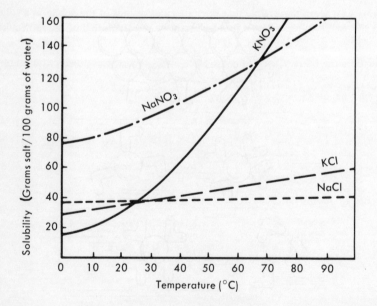

Fig. 7-4.   Solubility as a function of temperature when water is the solvent.

can be seen that at 100°C NaCl is least soluble and would crystallize first, while at 10° the initial precipitate would be KNO_3. Yet the original solution could be reproduced by replacing the evaporated water.

A reaction has been caused to take place by changing the physical conditions, but, more importantly, the general nature of reactions between ions has been indicated. Chemical reactions between ions in solution can be said to occur if particular ions are selectively removed from the solution through conversion to a precipitate, a gas or a nonionized molecule. It should go without saying that if the ion is changed into another ionic species or into the atoms characteristic of the elemental state a reaction has also taken place, but as we will see later these types of reaction are considered to be more than the simple interaction of ions.

There are many chemical compounds which can be studied, but first let us investigate the nature and properties of those inorganic molecules which we class as acids, bases and salts.

QUESTIONS FOR STUDY AND REVIEW

1. What would be the configuration of the valence electrons in the covalent molecules O_2, CO_2 and PH_3?

2. What would be the configuration of the valence electrons in the radicals PO_4^{-3}, HCO_3^- and NO_2^-?

3. Water in the liquid state appears to exist in the form $(H_2O)_x$, where x represents some number greater than 1. Explain.

4. Why does it seem reasonable that the molecules or ions of the solute in a solution should act independently in a fashion very similar to that of the molecules of a gas?

5. How does the battery used to cause electrolysis function as an electron pump?

Chapter 8

Acids, Bases, and Salts

Now that a background of atomic and ionic theory has been established, we are in a position to consider in greater detail the chemical properties of the three principal classes of inorganic compounds: acids, bases, and salts. Much of what is contained in this discussion will be applicable to organic compounds, but for the sake of simplicity we will not complicate the development of these concepts by attempting to make the definitions all-inclusive at this time. Attention will also be limited to interactions which take place in aqueous solutions, so that we must remember that water molecules make up the environment within which the other ions exist and react. In this circumstance, the polar nature of the water molecule assumes an important role.

8-1   Neutralization

A solution is described as being neutral with respect to its acidity or alkalinity if it contains neither an excess of acid nor of alkali, and pure water is the reference against which all other solutions are compared. In these terms an acid is defined as a molecule which forms hydrogen ions when dissolved in water, while an alkali provides hydroxyl ions. A typical neutralization reaction is then

$$HCl + NaOH \rightarrow NaCl + HOH$$

and the mixture of sodium chloride and water is neutral, as we could determine easily by any one of a number of laboratory procedures. But the reaction is actually not as simple as has been indicated in the reaction given, and the acid-alkali terminology is inadequate when the reaction is studied in greater detail.

8-2   Acids and Bases

We cannot begin to develop an acid-base theory which will have wide applicability until we have stated exactly what we mean by the words "acid" and "base." For our purposes, we will define an *acid* as a proton donor, and a *base* as a proton acceptor. The proton is, of course, that fundamental subatomic particle which is responsible for the positive charge of the nucleus. It has a unit charge of $+1$, and a mass on the atomic weight scale of 1.0079. More importantly, the proton is the nucleus of the hydrogen atom, and thus is identical with the hydrogen ion. It is almost certain that this particle never exists in the free state in the chemical systems which we will study, but there is no question but that a proton is transferred readily from one ion or molecule to another in a number of chemical reactions. Reactions of acids and bases then, always involve the transfer of a proton from donor to acceptor, and unless both are present, no reaction can occur. With these ideas in mind, we should re-examine the reaction between hydrochloric acid and sodium hydroxide. To begin with, each of the reactants has been dissolved in water; therefore we must begin by ascertaining what species exist in the solutions before they are mixed.

Hydrogen chloride, HCl, is a covalent molecule containing one atom of hydrogen and one atom of chlorine, and the bond between the atoms consists of two electrons, one supplied by each of the atoms involved. But the covalent bond in this molecule is a semipolar one. That is, the electrons are held more firmly by the chlorine than by the hydrogen, and also the proton provides a center of positive charge which makes the molecule nonsymmetrical. When this gas is dissolved in water, a reaction actually takes place between solute and solvent:

$$HCl + H_2O \rightarrow H_3O^+ + Cl^-$$

More than that, it is incorrect to indicate that the reaction goes from left to right, since we know that under certain circumstances and by certain procedures it is possible to separate the HCl and H_2O. It is true that in the solution there is very little, if any, HCl existing in the molecular form, but still we should write

$$HCl + H_2O = H_3O^+ + Cl^-$$

to indicate that the reaction is reversible. At the same time, it must be remembered that the water molecules which have reacted make up only a relatively small fraction of those present, and that the excess water molecules function as the solvent for the ions produced.

In the same manner, the solution of NaOH in water must be considered, but here we find that the process has followed a different path:

$$NaOH + H_2O = Na^+ + OH^- + H_2O$$

Of course, all of the ions formed are hydrated—that is, they carry with them a blanket of water molecules—but since all ions in solution have this same property, we do not indicate that hydration has occurred. There is no inconsistency in this, because the excess water serves only as a solvent and does not enter into the reaction.

Now, ignoring the water which is acting as a solvent, let us re-examine the reaction that takes place when the two solutions are mixed. One solution contains H_3O^+ (hydronium) and Cl^- ions, and the other contains Na^+ and OH^-:

$$H_3O^+ + Cl^- + Na^+ + OH^- = Na^+ + Cl^- + 2H_2O$$

As the Na^+ and Cl^- ions present in the original solutions are still to be found, unchanged, in the final one, it seems incorrect to indicate that they have participated in the reaction at all. The reaction that has actually taken place is not that given initially, but instead is

$$H_3O^+ + OH^- = 2H_2O$$

The acid in the solution of hydrochloric acid is H_3O^+, and the base in the solution of sodium hydroxide is OH^-. The neutralization reaction is the transfer of the proton from the acid, H_3O^+, to the base, OH^-, to form a molecule of water. We will find that water is not the only product of reactions of acids and bases, because there are other bases than the OH^- ion, but the transfer of the proton from one species to another is characteristic of acid-base interaction. The compounds that are commonly called acids are those which react with water to produce hydronium ions, and it is possible to classify them according to the degree to which the reaction proceeds. This does not refer to the speed with which the products are formed, but rather to the percentage of the original compound which is still present in the aqueous solution.

8-3 Strong and Weak Acids and Bases

Hydrochloric acid is a strong acid. When HCl is dissolved in water the reaction goes to completion. That is, the quantity of HCl still in the covalent form is negligible. Certain other acids are weak acids, and for them the reaction with water goes forward only partially and then stops, proceeding farther only if a base is added.

The formula HA can be used as a general formula for a weak acid. As this compound is dissolved in water it reacts with the solvent, but most of the acid may still be present as the molecule HA. Because our system of nomenclature defines an acid as a proton donor and a base as a proton acceptor, water is the base in the reaction which forms the hydronium ion. At the same time, the ionic species formed when HA loses a proton is a base, since, under proper conditions, that ion could accept a proton to become HA.

$$\underset{\text{Acid}}{HA} + \underset{\text{Base}}{H_2O} = \underset{\text{Acid}}{H_3O^+} + \underset{\text{Base}}{A^-}$$

An acid is a weak acid when the base corresponding to it is a strong base with a high affinity for protons.

Water has the unusual property of being able to act as either an acid or a base. If the salt NaA is dissolved in water there will be a slight reaction of A^- with water:

$$A^- + H_2O = HA + OH^-$$

and the water will be functioning as a proton donor. This reaction is one of *hydrolysis,* and can be considered as the reverse of neutralization in this particular reaction. We will see in subsequent chapters that the term has a wider application, yet the usage is consistent when the role played by water is assessed. In each instance a molecule of water is split, and the origin of the word lies in two roots: "hydro," for water, and "lysis," to split or divide. The degree to which hydrolysis occurs is determined by the relative strengths of the acid and the base. If the acid HA is a very weak one, the ion A^- must be classed as a strong base. This means that when the species A^- is added to water, a considerable number of the molecules HA will be produced, and the solution will become alkaline in its reaction.

The acidity or alkalinity of a solution is a measure of the excess of H_3O^+ or OH^- ions over the concentrations existing in pure water. Water is *amphoteric*—that is, it can act as either a proton donor or a proton acceptor; thus, pure water has equal concentrations of H_3O^+ and OH^- ions:

$$2H_2O = H_3O^+ + OH^-$$

Any aqueous solution, then, is defined as neutral when these ion concentrations are the same as those of water. These concentrations have been measured and found to be 10^{-7} moles per liter. That is, one liter of pure water contains 19×10^{-7} grams of H_3O^+ ion or, as we prefer to say, 1×10^{-7} gram molecular weights.

Such a number is inconvenient to use, and early in this century the Danish chemist Sørensen invented a scheme for expressing concentrations, which has been universally adopted. His suggestion was to use the terms pH and pOH to express the levels at which the ions existed. Each of these terms is the logarithm of the reciprocal of the ion concentration:

$$pH = \log \frac{1}{[H_3O]^+}$$

$$pOH = \log \frac{1}{[OH^-]}$$

The square brackets indicate that the concentration is to be expressed in moles per liter. Since the concentration of the hydronium ion in pure water is 10^{-7} moles per liter, the pH is 7:

$$pH = \log \frac{1}{[H_3O^+]} = \log \frac{1}{10^{-7}} = \log 10^7 = 7$$

In this way, we may more conveniently deal with statements of the acidity or basicity of aqueous solutions. An acidic solution is one whose pH is less than 7, and a basic solution has a pH greater than 7.

More time has been spent in discussing acids than will be devoted to bases, not because of their greater importance but simply because our definitions are based on acids as proton donors. There are two common bases: the hydroxyl ion, which is a strong base, and the ammonia molecule (or substituted ammonias in which other atoms have replaced one or two hydrogen atoms), a weak base. All of those compounds which we call hydroxides yield the hydroxyl ion when dissolved in water, while the ammonia-type base is common in biological systems.

8-4 Polybasic Acids

So far we have considered the transfer of only one proton from an acid to a base, but there are many *polybasic acids*—species which have more than one proton to donate. Each of these is capable of accepting one proton. Perhaps the best known of the polybasic acids is sulfuric acid, H_2SO_4. It is proper to consider the reaction of H_2SO_4 with water in two steps, even though both H_2SO_4 and HSO_4^- are strong acids, because we know of the existence of the HSO_4^- ion:

$$H_2SO_4 + H_2O = H_3O^+ + HSO_4^-$$
$$HSO_4^- + H_2O = H_3O^+ + SO_4^{-2}$$

Anyone who has read the label for any of the well-advertised toilet bowl cleansers is aware of this acid. It is perhaps easier to talk about weaker polybasic acids, however, because there are implications which go beyond the sequential ionization to which we have just referred.

Phosphoric acid, H_3PO_4, is a polybasic acid that can be categorized both as a strong and as a weak acid. It is potentially a donor of three protons, but the third is given up only with great reluctance. We can write reactions for phosphoric acid which are comparable to those given for sulfuric acid:

$$H_3PO_4 + H_2O = H_2PO_4^- + H_3O^+$$
$$H_2PO_4^- + H_2O = HPO_4^{-2} + H_3O^+$$
$$HPO_4^{-2} + H_2O = PO_4^{-3} + H_3O^+$$

but the ion HPO_4^{-2} is such a weak acid that only a minute quantity of the PO_4^{-3} ion is present in a solution of phosphoric acid. However, if a base is added that will combine with the H_3O^+ ion, the acid can be neutralized, and a compound such as Na_3PO_4 can be formed; the reaction occurs in three steps:

$$NaOH + H_3PO_4 = NaH_2PO_4 + H_2O$$
$$NaOH + NaH_2PO_4 = Na_2HPO_4 + H_2O$$
$$NaOH + Na_2HPO_4 = Na_3PO_4 + H_2O$$

8-5 Hydrolysis and Neutralization

Anyone who has used TSP (trisodium phosphate, Na_3PO_4) as a floor or wall cleanser is well aware of the action of the solution on the knuckles. The explanation for this physiological effect lies in the strength of phosphoric acid as an acid, or rather in the basic strength of the PO_4^{-3} ion. The introduction of Na_3PO_4 into a volume of water results in the formation of Na^+ and PO_4^{-3} ions. But the PO_4^{-3} ion is a relatively strong base, so that hydrolysis occurs with the production of OH^- ions:

$$PO_4^{-3} + H_2O = HPO_4^- + OH^-$$

The resulting solution is so strongly alkaline that its concurrent corrosive action is subsequently apparent. As this equation indicates, hydrolysis can be viewed as the reverse of neutralization.

A consideration of the degree to which hydrolysis occurs in this circumstance also leads to the interesting observation that certain ions have the capacity to act both as an acid and as a base. The ions $H_2PO_4^-$ and HPO_4^{-2} will, under the proper set of conditions, act as proton donors (neutralization) or, in a different environment, may be proton acceptors (hydrolysis). This phenomenon can better be discussed after we have investigated equilibria generally, so we will delay any discussion in depth until that topic has been considered.

8-6 Salts: The Product of Neutralization

There should, however, be some mention of a class of compounds which have been often alluded to but never named. The reaction of an acid on a base results in the transfer of a proton from one species to another, but at the same time there are ions in the solution which take no active part in the neutralization. As has been indicated, the equation for the reaction can be written without involving these ions at all, and yet, if the final solution is evaporated, a compound is formed which contains these ions as constituent parts. The compound so formed is termed a *salt* (Fig. 8-1). Any definition is inadequate, but we can come close to including all salts in a class which is described as being formed in the course of a neutralization reaction from the non-proton portion of the acid and the ion originally associated with the base. These substances are distinguished by the fact that they are ionic in nature and display chemical properties characteristic of both of the ions present in the molecular formulas. A large part of inorganic chemistry is concerned with the interaction of these ions, and it is with these substances, as well as with acids and bases, that we will concern ourselves in the considerations of chemical energetics and equilibria which follow.

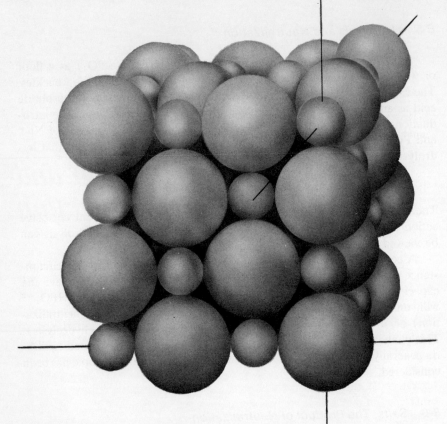

Fig. 8-1.   A drawing of the sodium chloride lattice. The smaller spheres represent sodium ions, the larger represent chloride ions. (From Brown, General Chemistry, Charles E. Merrill Books, Inc., 1963, p. 91.)

QUESTIONS FOR STUDY AND REVIEW

1. Complete and balance the equations for the following neutralization reactions:

$$Ca(OH)_2 + H_3PO_4 \rightarrow$$
$$H_2SO_4 + Al(OH)_3 \rightarrow$$
$$NH_4OH + HNO_3 \rightarrow$$

2. What would be the basic ion and what would be the acid ion supplied by liquid ammonia acting as a solvent?

3. If a solution containing 1/10 mole per liter of an acid has a pH of 3, would the acid be classed as strong or weak? What percentage of the acid is ionized?

4. If a solution containing 1 mole per liter of salt has a pH of 8, what percentage of the salt is hydrolyzed?

Chapter 9

Energetics, Oxidation and Reduction

The fact that energy may be liberated when chemical reactions occur is demonstrated daily in thousands of backyard barbecues, and it is not difficult to think of a number of other examples comparable to the combination of charcoal and oxygen. It is less obvious that energy may be absorbed in some interactions, but a logical analysis should indicate that such is at least a possibility. Molecules and ions do have measurable energy levels, and the conversion of those entities into others results in either the absorption or liberation of energy depending upon the relative energy contents of reactants and products. Since in most reactions energy is involved in the form that we know as heat, we will limit our discussion to *heats of reaction,* which we will evaluate quantitatively in terms of calories absorbed or set free. When interactions occur between atoms, molecules, or ions, the changes which take place are changes in the bonding of atoms to one another. The energy of a reaction then is an expression of the changes in energy content of the chemical bonds that are formed or disrupted. This means that we will be concerned with changes of a chemical, and not a physical, nature.

9-1 Heats of Reaction

If energy is liberated in the course of a chemical reaction, we describe that reaction as being *exothermic,* and we recognize that the total energy content of the molecules formed is less than that of the reactants. On the other hand, if energy is absorbed, the reaction is described as being *endothermic.* A particular example of each is not difficult to find, but let us consider in some detail the reaction between the elements hydrogen and oxygen which results in the formation of water. If this reaction is carried out so that the heat liberated can be measured, the reaction can be written

$$2H_2 + O_2 \rightarrow 2H_2O + 119,200 \text{ calories}$$

and we see that the reaction is an exothermic one. The quantity of heat released is on the basis of gram-molecular weights for the reaction as written above, so that the formation of 36 grams of water results in the liberation of 119,200 calories. If we wish to prepare hydrogen and oxygen by bringing about the decomposition of water, we must introduce a quantity of energy into the system equal to that which was liberated in the formation of water, and the equation is

$$2H_2O \rightarrow 2H_2 + O_2 - 119,200 \text{ calories}$$

Convention calls for an endothermic reaction to be designated in the form just written, rather than by having the heat of reaction appear as a positive value on the left side of the equation.

A consideration of the heat liberated in reactions lends support to certain of the statements which have been made previously about reactions between ions. When pure compounds are dissolved in water, this process is often accompanied by an increase or a decrease in temperature. Heat is evolved or absorbed as the ions or molecules form bonds with the molecules of solvent, and we speak of the *heat of solution* of the particular substance. If we now mix two solutions, we find that there may be no heat change at all; but if a reaction does take place, the heat of reaction is independent of those ions in the solution that do not enter into the reaction. We have stated that the neutralization of an acid and a base is a reaction between hydronium and hydroxyl ions. If the heat of neutralization is measured, the heat of formation of water from these ions can be determined. The reactions in Table 9-1 show that the heat of reaction for the formation of water from its ions is 15,400 calories per mole, and that the nature of the other ions present has no effect. These figures are only valid, of course, provided that the reactants have already been dissolved in water so that there is no heat of solution involved.

Table 9-1

HCl	$+ NaOH$	$\rightarrow H_2O$	$+ NaCl$	$+ 15,400$ cal
H_2SO_4	$+ 2NaOH$	$\rightarrow 2H_2O$	$+ Na_2SO_4$	$+ 30,800$ cal
HNO_3	$+ KOH$	$\rightarrow H_2O$	$+ KNO_3$	$+ 15,400$ cal

The reaction which is taking place in each case is

$$H_3O^+ + OH^- \rightarrow 2H_2O + 15,400 \text{ cal}$$

Heats of reaction are additive, and the formation of compounds that are intermediates demonstrates this conclusively:

$$2C + O_2 \rightarrow 2CO + 52,800 \text{ cal}$$
$$2CO + O_2 \rightarrow 2CO_2 + 136,000 \text{ cal}$$
$$2C + 2O_2 \rightarrow 2CO_2 + 188,800 \text{ cal}$$

The total heat evolved in the formation of carbon dioxide from carbon and oxygen is independent of the route which is taken. This conservation of energy in chemical reactions is as fundamental as is the conservation of mass, and, although physicists have demonstrated conclusively that energy and mass are interconvertible, the conservation concepts are valid so long as we apply them to carefully defined circumstances.

The *heat of formation* for a chemical compound is an indicator of the stability of the molecule or of the ions of which that compound is composed. Carbon dioxide is a very stable substance because a great deal of energy must be introduced into it in order that the molecule be separated into the atoms of which it is composed. Sodium chloride—or more correctly, the sodium and chloride ions—possesses a high degree of stability as indicated by the large quantity of heat which is liberated when it is formed from the elements sodium and chlorine. But why then, if the heat of formation of water is so great, do mixtures of hydrogen and oxygen gas remain unreacted unless a spark is introduced? The answer is simple. The reaction of hydrogen and oxygen requires that the molecules of the elements have a high energy content since the molecules H_2 and O_2 are themselves stable, with positive heats of reaction. The reaction must be initiated by first raising some small number of molecules of each gas to a sufficiently high temperature. Then the heat evolved from this initial reaction is great enough to cause others to react. The net result is a chain reaction, really a continually escalating combination. If the reaction is exceedingly rapid, we use the term "explosion" to describe it.

If we look at a reaction as it occurs, we can present the information graphically as shown in Fig. 9-1. We can suppose that the reaction concerned is a general one which can be expressed as

$$A + B \rightarrow C + D$$

Because the reactants A and B have an energy content that is higher than that of the products, the reaction is an exothermic one; and yet A and B can be mixed together at ordinary temperatures without any reaction taking place. The *activation energy* is that quantity of energy which must be introduced into the system to cause the reaction to begin (the discharge from the spark plug in an automobile engine, for example), after which time the reaction takes place without the further introduction of energy. This energy of activation may be large, as in the case of gasoline and oxygen, or it may be very small—nitroglycerine, for example, can be exploded by a very small shock. Stability in a chemical compound is determined by its heat of formation, its heat of activation, or both.

9-2 Catalysts

In certain instances the activation energy can be lowered by some substance which itself does not enter into the reaction. Any substance which

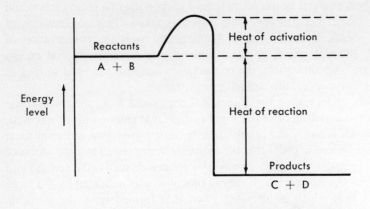

Fig. 9-1.   **Energy diagram for the reaction A + B → C + D.**

affects the rate of a chemical reaction, without itself changing in that reaction, is called a *catalyst*. Most of the catalysts which are commonly dealt with have a positive effect, accelerating the rate of the reaction by lowering the activation energy. That is, they lower the activation energy hump shown in Fig. 9-1 so that the reaction takes place more readily than it would in the absence of the catalyst. There are many examples of such an action; we will discuss some of these at greater length when we deal with enzymes in biological systems. But before we leave the subject of energy relations in chemical reactions we should look into the practical effects of exothermic reactions.

9-3   Fuels and Explosives

All of those chemical compounds which we call fuels undergo combinations with oxygen to produce energy in a usable form, and at such a rate that utilization is possible. The difference between a fuel and an explosive is often no more than the rate at which energy is released. The compounds most commonly in use are those with a high carbon and hydrogen content, because the production of carbon dioxide and water is accompanied by the release of large quantities of heat. Coal, wood and petroleum have been the principal substances employed, and, while they have been adequate for most industrial requirements, they have limitations in applications to rockets where the release of energy must be very rapid. The principal shortcoming has been that it is not possible to supply a sufficient quantity of oxygen to the site of the reaction. A great deal of research has been conducted in an attempt to perfect systems that will provide oxygen for combustion, and also to use elements other than oxygen as the agent which makes the exothermic reaction possible. The principal problem in handling such substances used—as elemental fluorine, oxides of nitrogen and nitric acid, and solid oxidants—has revolved around their extreme chemical reactivity. They not only combine chemically with the fuel, but also react with the container.

Explosives may fall into either of two categories. There are compounds which are inherently unstable because of their negative heat of formation, and there are mixtures of compounds which simply provide a fuel and an oxidant in a more or less stable solid form. The best example of the former is nitroglycerine. The decomposition of this molecule releases a relatively large quantity of energy, and the products of the decomposition are gases. The sudden production of large quantities of very hot gases in a confined space produces an outward force which is very large. The black powder used for so many years achieved a similar result in a different fashion. This explosive was a mixture of oxidizable materials (carbon and sulfur) with an oxygen-containing molecule (potassium nitrate, KNO_3). When started, the reaction would take place very rapidly, once again with the production of gaseous compounds and with the evolution of large quantities of heat. The net result was the same, except that the rate of the second reaction was slower and the energy released per unit weight was less, so that black powder was eventually replaced by more efficient explosives.

It would be well to distinguish between the fuels and explosives, which are effective because of the energy released in chemical reactions, and their nuclear counterparts. Chemical reactions, involving only the outer electrons in the atom, are very small in energy release as compared with those interactions which involve the nucleus. The principle is the same; energy is released at a rapid or a controlled rate depending upon the effect desired, but the quantity is drastically different. The binding energy involved in holding the nucleus together is far, far greater than that of the electrons of the atom. The distinction is sometimes made that the nuclear explosion is greater because mass is being converted to energy. The same is true of a chemical reaction, but the decrease in mass is simply too small to be observed. The flashlight battery which provides the energy to produce the emergent beam of light is losing mass as energy is radiated, but the decrease is beyond the limits of our measuring devices. Rates of reaction and total amount of energy released are both involved, but the principle nonetheless remains the same.

9-4 Oxidation and Reduction

As has been previously noted, chemical interactions of atoms involve transformations in the arrangements of the electrons which lie in the outermost valence shells. Historically the term "oxidation" was applied to those reactions in which some material combined with oxygen, and no distinction was drawn to distinguish between reactions of elements and compounds. At the same time it was recognized that there were reactions of a different nature which involved either the removal of oxygen or the addition of hydrogen. An example of the former is the removal of oxygen, by its combination with carbon, from an oxide to form a metal, while the addition of hydrogen is almost exclusively confined to the reaction of organic materials with elemental hydrogen. However, as the understanding of atomic structure became more sophisticated, there arose a growing recognition that a greater consistency in classification could be achieved if the reactions were viewed in terms of the valence changes of the atoms or ions involved. This meant that the terms oxidation and reduction were given specific definitions lacking previously, so that oxidation came to identify an increase in positive or a decrease in negative valence, while reduction was the opposite of oxidation. A corollary of this redefinition was the acceptance of the concept that oxidation could not take place alone, because if one atom increased in valence, another must of necessity decrease.

In the framework of modern atomic theory a change in valence is understood as a gain or loss of electrons in ions or a change in the number of shared electrons in coordinate bonding. Accordingly we find that chemical theory has now provided a newer and more precise definition for the terms. A material is oxidized when it loses electrons, and it is reduced when it gains electrons. Of course, one process is not possible without the other, since the electrons removed from one entity must, according to our conservation laws, be added to another. This does not mean that oxidation and reduction can be considered separately. Instead, we now find that we have more freedom in dealing conceptually with reactions than before. Many reactions can now be divided into two parts called half-reactions, and the complete reaction is nothing more than the combination of the two half-reactions into one balanced expression. This allows us to make more sense of the manner in which electrolysis takes place since in this instance, the reactions are separated widely in space—far more than is possible if the direct interaction of atoms or ions is assumed.

9-5   Half-Reactions

Instead of attempting to use reactions of oxygen to exemplify the oxidation-reduction concept, let us use the reaction for the formation and decomposition of sodium chloride. Compounds of oxygen are covalent in nature, and while we will see later that our ideas are equally viable in circumstances of this type, it will be easier to begin with reactions in which electron transfer actually occurs. When elemental sodium and chlorine react, there is a transfer of electrons from one atom to another, but the oxidation-reduction view allows us to look at each element individually. A sodium atom is oxidized, according to our definition, since it loses an electron and increases in positive valence:

$$Na^0 \rightarrow Na^+ + e^-$$

This then is the half-reaction of oxidation. At the same time, the chlorine atom loses an electron, but because the element exists in the diatomic state the half-reaction is written

$$Cl_2 + 2e^- \rightarrow 2Cl^-$$

and the overall reaction, a combination of the half-reactions, must result in electron balance. Combining the two makes balancing the reaction necessary, and this is brought about by doubling the number of sodium atoms being oxidized:

$$2Na \rightarrow 2Na^+ + 2e^-$$
$$Cl_2 + 2e^- \rightarrow 2Cl^-$$

If we add them together a complete reaction is symbolized:

$$2Na + Cl_2 + 2e^- \rightarrow 2Na^+ + 2Cl^- + 2e^-$$

But since the two electrons appear on both sides of the equation there has been no net change. The electrons may be eliminated and the equation is conventionally presented as

$$2Na + Cl_2 \rightarrow 2Na^+ + 2Cl^-$$

or

$$2Na + Cl_2 \rightarrow 2NaCl$$

The electrolysis of sodium chloride to form the elements may be carried out readily by the passage of an electric current through the molten salt or through an aqueous solution (Fig. 9-2). This is a common procedure for the preparation of a number of other metals as well, particularly such reactive ones as aluminum and magnesium. In this instance reactions of oxidation take place, but the transfer of electrons is indirect rather than direct. An

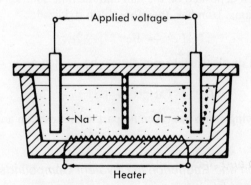

Fig. 9-2. **Electrolysis of molten sodium chloride.**

external source accomplishes the removal of electrons from one ion and the supply of them to the other. The half-reactions are the reverse of those presented above, and in the case of sodium chloride, sodium ions are reduced:

$$Na^+ + e^- \rightarrow Na^0$$

and chloride ions are oxidized:

$$2Cl^- \rightarrow Cl_2 + 2e^-$$

The reactions can take place separated in space because a mechanism is supplied which transports the electrons from the site at which the oxidation takes place to that at which the reduction occurs. This reaction does not take place spontaneously, of course, because the original formation of the ions was an exothermic process. Accordingly, energy must be supplied to the system so that the reverse reactions can be forced to take place. As might be expected, vast stores of electrical power are required for the manufacture of elements such as sodium and chlorine and others of the highly reactive elements.

9-6   Replacement Reactions

If, instead of the reactions of direct combustion or decomposition, we look at those which are classified as replacement we find that the ideas of oxidation and reduction are equally tenable. When an iron nail is placed into a solution of copper sulfate, the nail becomes plated with copper. It is not difficult to see that at least one portion of the overall reaction is the transformation of Cu^{++} to Cu^0, since eventually the characteristic blue color of the cupric ion will disappear. The conversion of the cupric ion into copper metal is a reduction, and the half-reaction is

$$Cu^{++} + 2e^- \rightarrow Cu^0$$

Copper has been deposited on the nail and the final solution can be shown to contain Fe^{++} ions. Iron has, therefore, been oxidized:

$$Fe^0 \rightarrow Fe^{++} + 2e^-$$

and the overall displacement reaction can be written as an oxidation-reduction reaction:

$$Fe^0 + Cu^{++} \rightarrow Fe^{++} + Cu^0$$

The accompanying anion has taken no part in the reaction and so need not be indicated.

9-7   Oxidation and Reduction in Covalent Compounds

When our new definitions are extended to include those elements that react to form covalent bonds, we must modify the concept, because electrons are not actually gained or lost. Now the valence or, as it might better be called, the oxidation state is determined by the number of electrons shared by the atom in question. This is the case whether the bond is a covalent or a coordinate one. In the radicals $SO_4^=$ and $SO_3^=$, the oxidation states of the sulfur atom are six and four, respectively. We will see later that this rule is inadequate to deal with the case of the carbon atom, which has the special property of forming double or triple bonds with other atoms.

All of the foregoing does not mean that the peculiar role of oxygen has been forgotten. The chemical combination of the element oxygen with other substances is an oxidation; in our new definition, the word has simply been given a more limited meaning. Reactions which take place in nature are often more complicated than are those which are caused to occur in the laboratory, since natural conditions are not carefully controlled. It is interesting to note the role which water plays in a great many of the reactions which involve oxygen. In very dry climates oxidative changes take place very slowly, and it appears as if the intimate contact produced when a solution forms accelerates the rate. Of course, no material is completely insoluble, so that in many instances the reaction is taking place between ions or atoms in solution; and, as we have seen, such interactions do take place more rapidly and easily than do most reactions in the solid state.

On several occasions in past chapters, reference has been made to rates of reaction. It is perhaps time that we looked specifically at the manner in which reactions occur, and consider in some greater detail the degree to which reactions may be reversed or go to completion.

QUESTIONS FOR STUDY AND REVIEW

1. What is meant when we speak of the heat of formation of a compound?

2. How can we explain the fact that many compounds appear to be reasonably stable even though a great deal of heat is evolved when they decompose?

3. If we were to define an explosive as a molecule which decomposes with the release of energy, why would it be incorrect to use the phrase "atomic explosion"?

4. Sketch a figure comparable to Fig. 9-1 for the explosion of an explosive such as the smokeless powder in a shotgun shell.

5. How does scientific usage of the term "catalyst" compare with everyday use?

6. What are the essential differences in our use of the terms combustion and oxidation?

Chapter 10

Reaction Rates and Equilibrium

The rate at which a chemical reaction takes place is described in terms of the quantity of product formed or of reactant which disappears per unit time. In many instances the rate is exceedingly rapid, so much so that special equipment must be devised to follow the progress of the transformation. This is particularly true when the reactants are ions, and a simple collision is all that is necessary to effect the interactions. For other reactions the rate is much slower, particularly when the reacting species are sizable molecules which must undergo complicated rearrangements and must approach each other in a special spatial relationship if they are to do more than rebound unchanged. However, certain observations can be made which apply to all reactions: statements about physical factors, independent of the reactants, which affect the rate at which reactions take place.

10-1 Reaction Rates

Chemical interactions obviously can occur only if the molecules or ions involved come into contact one with another. The formation of chemical bonds is impossible over distances which are large in comparison with the size of the molecules themselves. Accordingly, any change in physical conditions which will increase the number of collisions per unit time will speed up the reaction. As we have seen before, an increase in temperature on a macroscopic scale is equivalent to a greater speed of travel at the molecular level. A rise in temperature, with a concomitant speeding up of motion of the molecules, will increase the probability of collision and so the probability of chemical interaction. A general rule of thumb, in use for more than one hundred years, is that the rate at which a chemical reaction takes place is approximately doubled when the temperature is raised $10°C$. It should also be obvious that if the number of interacting particles is increased, there should be a greater possibility of collision and, thus, a greater possibility for interaction. This latter phenomenon is somewhat more complicated, particularly when more than two individual particles are involved in the formation of a product, and we must deal with it at greater length later on in our discussion.

Mention must also be made of those materials called catalysts, which have been discussed previously. A positive catalyst speeds up a reaction because it forms some transient intermediate that is more reactive than the original species. Such an effect is often a surface one, in which the interacting molecules or atoms are brought into contact by virtue of their being held closely on the surface, or it may be because the activation energy has been reduced. In certain reactions, the catalyst may be effective because there is actually some compound formed which is able to react more easily. The action of a catalyst, which does result in some modification of the original system, will not be considered at great length here. It will be referred to again when we deal further with biological systems. But for now let us take another look at what has already been said about reactions and the manner in which they occur.

10-2   Reversible Reactions

If we write a hypothetical reaction as we have done before:

$$A + B \rightarrow C + D$$

what is indicated is the interaction of two particles, A and B, to form two new particles, C and D. When we deal with those real systems for which our measuring instruments are applicable, we must recognize that we are dealing with large numbers of A's and B's and that all are not interacting simultaneously. We must also consider the possibility that the reaction as written is reversible, so that C and D can react to re-form A and B. Such a possibility is feasible from the point of view of chemical energetics even if the reaction is an exothermic one, because the reversal requires only that the necessary amount of energy be introduced into the system to cause the reaction to take place. In actual fact many reactions can be reversed only with great difficulty, but since many others are readily reversible, let us consider that our example is one of those which can go in either direction with relative ease.

Let us consider the changes that take place in a system after some finite quantity of A and B are added. Initially, with only A and B present, the reaction to form C and D takes place at a rate which is proportional to the concentrations of A and B. Mathematically we can describe what is going on by saying that the speed of the reaction is proportional to the product of the concentrations of A and B. We will use square brackets, [ ], to indicate that we are talking about concentration in terms of moles (gram molecular weights) per liter. For the chemical equation A + B → C + D, the speed of the reaction is proportional to the concentrations of the reactants,

$S_1 \propto$ [A] [B]. But the concentrations of A and B are constantly decreasing, so the value of S is becoming progressively smaller. If the reverse reaction did not occur, the amount of each reactant present would approach so close to zero that we could no longer detect its presence.

But suppose that the reverse reaction does take place readily under the prevailing conditions. Initially, with no C or D present, there would be no formation of A and B. But as the reactants on the left form the products on the right, the reverse reaction will take place more and more rapidly. Once again, the rate will be proportional to the concentration, so for the reaction C + D $\rightarrow$ A + B we have the proportionality $S_2 \propto$ [C] [D]. There are now two processes taking place, one tending to decrease the concentrations of A and B and the other to increase them. The same is true for C and D. It is not enough to know that proportionalities and tendencies exist: instead our goal is to quantify our understanding so that we may describe the system mathematically. A proportionality may be converted to an equality by the introduction of an appropriate constant, and so, for a specified temperature (remember that rates of reaction are altered by changes in temperature), we can write the equation

$$S_1 = k_1[A] [B] \quad \text{and} \quad S_2 = k_2[C] [D]$$

where k_1 and k_2 are the rate constants for the particular reactions. As we have seen, the values of S change with time as concentrations change, but k_1 and k_2 have fixed values for a certain reaction at a given temperature.

10-3   Systems at Equilibrium

Let us go farther and examine graphically the manner in which the values for S_1 and S_2 vary with the passage of time. In Fig. 10-1 are plotted the reac-

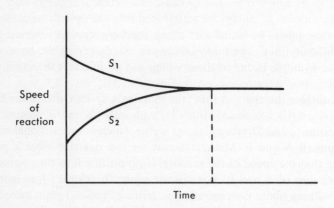

Fig. 10-1.   The variation of the speeds of a reaction and its reverse as it approaches, and finally reaches, equilibrium.

tion rates S_1 and S_2 as a function of time. As indicated previously, when A and B react to form C and D, the speed of reaction of the former pair decreases and that of the latter pair increases. At some point in time, A and B are disappearing as rapidly as they are appearing. There can then be no further change in the speeds at which the reactions occur because there will no longer be any variation in the concentrations of A and B or of C and D. We describe the system now as being one which is in *equilibrium*. A chemical equilibrium is characterized by being a *dynamic equilibrium:* the overall composition of the system remains unchanged, yet at the same time reactions are going on at very appreciable rates. Mathematically we can now say that $S_1 = S_2$.

When this equality exists, then

$$k_1[A][B] = k_2[C][D] \tag{1}$$

and this equation can be rearranged to read

$$\frac{k_1}{k_2} = \frac{[C][D]}{[A][B]} \tag{2}$$

Often it is extremely difficult to determine reaction rates, and accordingly rate constants are seldom determined. It is not necessary that we know them, however, because as shown in Eq. (2) the ratio of the rate constants is equal to a proportion made up of expressions of the concentrations of the reactants and the products of our chemical reaction. Since one constant divided by another can be equated to a third constant, $k_1/k_2 = K_{E_1}$, where K_E is the equilibrium constant. This latter term can be determined if the various concentrations can be measured when the system has achieved equilibrium, and for most systems this is a relatively easy procedure. The equilibrium constant is a number which expresses the ratios of concentrations, and is unvarying so long as the temperature remains unchanged:

$$K_E = \frac{[C][D]}{[A][B]} \tag{3}$$

When the equilibrium is disturbed either by the addition or removal of a quantity of one of the reacting species, one of the reactions will be speeded up or slowed down. In Fig. 10-2, the equilibrium is upset by the introduction of a small quantity of the reactant A at time t. Initially the reaction $A + B \rightarrow C + D$ will be speeded up, but the rate will gradually become slower as the concentrations of A and B are decreased. Concurrently C and D will increase in concentration so that the rate of the reverse reaction will gradually increase. Eventually, the two rates will become equal once more, although at a changed level, and an equilibrium will be re-established. The concentrations in the system now are different than they were before, but the final levels will give the same numerical value for the equilibrium constant. The addition of a catalyst to the system will not change the final equilibrium, but will shorten the time required for its establishment, since both reactions will be speeded up to the same degree.

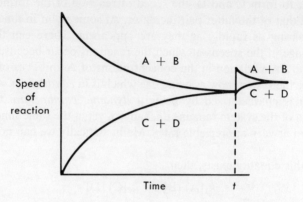

Fig. 10-2. The temporary disturbance of a system at equilibrium brought about by the introduction of an additional quantity of reactant A, and the subsequent attainment of a new equilibrium.

Equilibria may exist in either the liquid or the gaseous state. If one or more of the reactants are gases, the concentration of the reactants can be changed by increasing the pressure. In the gaseous state there will be crowding of the molecules and so an increase in concentration, while in the two phase liquid-gas system, where the equilibrium is in the liquid, the increased solubility of the gas at a higher pressure will place more molecules in a position to participate in the reaction.

We will find that equilibria are very important in biological systems, but we must distinguish between an equilibrium state and the *steady state* which is characteristic of living organisms. An equilibrium can exist only when it is isolated and has no contact or interchange of matter or energy with the outside environment. But organisms do not exist in this fashion; living things are constantly taking in nutriment and are excreting waste products. The overall composition of the organism does not change, but there is interchange of matter and energy with the surroundings. We describe this as a steady state made up of a series of equilibria, with each of these constantly readjusting to compensate for the changes taking place.

10-4 Buffer Systems

One group of equilibria is of particular interest since its members control the hydrogen-ion concentration in the body fluids of living organisms. These equilibria are called *buffer systems,* or *buffers,* because they absorb the shock to the solution of the introduction of quantities of acids or bases and keep the acidity of the fluid at a level that the organism can tolerate. Buffers are mixtures of a weak acid and a salt of that acid, or a weak base and a salt of that base, and they function because of the equilibrium that exists between the acid and its conjugate base, or the base and its conjugate acid. Let us choose, as an example, a particular one from among the many which are found in the blood plasma of animals, although it must be recognized that quantitatively this is not the most important.

In an earlier chapter, we saw that phosphoric acid is a polybasic acid which ionizes in steps to give the ions $H_2PO_4^-$ and $HPO_4^=$. When these two ions are in solution together, they form an equilibrium according to the equation

$$H_2PO_4^- + H_2O = H_3O^+ + HPO_4^= \qquad (4)$$

and the equilibrium constant for this system is written as

$$K_E = \frac{[H_3O^+][HPO_4^=]}{[H_2PO_4^-][H_2O]} \qquad (5)$$

The tolerable level for the H_3O^+ ion for the blood plasma of an animal lies in the range of 1×10^{-7} to 3×10^{-7} moles per liter. In the process of metabolism, when compounds are produced that would raise or lower the concentration beyond these limits, the phosphate buffer system (and all of the others present) readjust to control the level. As can be seen from Eq. (4), an increase in the concentration of the H_3O^+ ion will increase the rate of the reaction from right to left. The final state of the equilibrium will be reached when Eq. (5) is once more satisfied mathematically. If the concentrations of $H_2PO_4^-$ and $HPO_4^=$ are large compared with H_3O^+, then the final concentration of the latter will not be significantly altered. A similar statement can be evolved if some base is introduced which reacts with the hydronium ion to lower its concentration.

10-5 Temperature Effects on Equilibria

These reactions which can be so readily manipulated at low temperatures are ones for which the heats of reaction are relatively low. In general, a reaction which is highly exothermic goes so nearly to completion that it is very difficult to demonstrate that an equilibrium actually exists. When hydrogen combines with oxygen to form water, the reaction produces 59,600 calories for each mole of water produced. This means that the decomposition of water into hydrogen and oxygen would require the introduction into the system of that amount of heat, and at a temperature of 100°C very little free H_2 and O_2 would be in equilibrium with gaseous H_2O. However, if the temperature is raised to 2000°C the reaction

$$2H_2O \rightarrow 2H_2 + O_2$$

would be encouraged and the equilibrium system would contain significant amounts of the elemental gases. We find that equilibria are shifted with increases in temperature in the direction of the endothermic reaction.

Now that we have established some background of atomic structure, heats of reaction, and equilibrium, let us look at the manner in which substances interact in those energy-producing or absorbing reactions that we refer to as oxidation-reduction.

QUESTIONS FOR STUDY AND REVIEW

1. The rates of heterogeneous reactions proceed much more slowly than homogeneous ones because the surface available for interaction is so small. Suggest why powdered sugar dissolves in water more quickly than granulated sugar.

2. Some reactions proceed by "autocatalysis." Such reactions tend to accelerate with time and get out of control. What does autocatalysis mean and how can one explain these observations?

3. Why does a sugar cube dissolve in a liquid faster if it is stirred than otherwise?

4. Describe the state of affairs when a system is in equilibrium. What distinguishes static and dynamic equilibria? Is there a situation where the chemical equilibrium could become static?

5. The carbonate buffer is important in the body:

$$H_2CO_3 + H_2O = H_3O^+ + HCO_3^-$$

As the acidity in the bloodstream rises, one yawns, thus releasing extra carbon dioxide. In aqueous solution CO_2 is known as carbonic acid, or H_2CO_3. Show how the ideas of rate and equilibrium relate to this process.

Chapter 11

The Chemistry of Carbon

Until 1825 the prevailing scientific opinion was that compounds which had their origin in living systems could not be synthesized because the vital force of life was necessary for their formation. All of these organic substances are based on the carbon atom, so that even though Wohler demonstrated that the heat-induced rearrangement of the inorganic ammonium isocyanate, NH_4NCO, produced the organic urea, NH_2—CO—NH_2, the study of carbon compounds is still termed organic chemistry. Today organic chemistry is not limited to compounds of natural origin, but still revolves around the covalent carbon atom. The complexity of the subject comes from the property of the carbon atom which makes possible covalent bonding between carbon atoms, with the formation of structures of almost infinite variety in size and arrangement.

Of course, all of the preceding discussions about acids and bases, oxidation and reduction, and especially rates of reaction and equilibrium are as applicable to organic molecules as they are to inorganic ones. In fact, considerations of rates of reaction and equilibrium are of particular interest since, with the complex structures common in organic chemistry, reactions are often determined and directed by the manner in which the molecules approach one another. No longer are we dealing with simple ions which need only collide to react. In addition, there are many occasions when more than one reaction is possible, and the interaction which predominates is determined by both the chemical and physical environment into which the compounds are placed. Types of compounds, and types of reactions, are so numerous that only a select few can be mentioned, but we shall see that the laws and concepts applicable to inorganic chemistry can be applied to organic and biological chemistry as well.

11-1   Saturated Hydrocarbons

In terms of the variety of types of atoms, the simple compounds are the hydrocarbons, in which the molecules contain only carbon and hydrogen atoms. These are the substances that make up the major fraction of petro-leum. All are covalently bonded; and let us consider initially those which have only single bonds (one pair of shared electrons) between carbon atoms. The simplest of these compounds is methane, CH_4.

The valence bonds of the carbon atom are so located that the molecule of methane has a tetrahedral shape, with carbon at the center and hydrogen at the apexes. The formula CH_4 represents correctly the number of atoms in the molecule, but does not give any indication of spatial arrangement. Since the reproduction of a three-dimensional structure on a two-dimensional page is accomplished only with difficulty (Fig. 11-1), we will make use of a

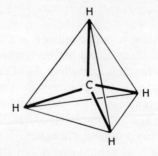

Fig. 11-1. A three-dimensional representation of the methane molecule showing the tetrahedral shape of the bonds of the carbon atom.

more easily followed representation. This picture, the *structural formula,* is valid so long as we remember that it is two-dimensional, and that it cannot be lifted from the page for our examination. It can be rotated but not turned over, for the latter maneuver would lift the model into a dimension in which it does not exist according to our convention. The structural formula of methane is

with each short line indicating a pair of electrons shared between the atoms linked. For inorganic compounds the question of the spatial arrangement of atoms seldom arises, although we have seen that it can be of importance for a molecule of water. For organic molecules, however, the relative posi-tions of the atoms are often of primary concern.

The necessity for the use of structural formulas and the corollary re-quirement for a system of nomenclature is dictated by the exceedingly large number of organic compounds. The possibility of different arrangements of atoms leads to a recognition of the existence of *isomers,* molecules with the same number of atoms of each type but with a different spatial arrangement. The reader can imagine the large number of isomers which can exist as the size of the molecule increases. As the number of recognized compounds increases it becomes apparent that some agreed upon system of naming them is required if confusion is not to develop. Trivial names, which are individual labels applied to particular compounds, would become so numerous that no one would be able to remember all of them. Accordingly, an international meeting of chemists in Switzerland adopted the Geneva system of nomenclature, which brought order into organic chemistry. Let us look at the series of compounds listed in Table 11-1.

We find that for methane, etane, propane, butane, and pentane, each molecule differs from the preceding one by a CH_2 group. Such a series, in which each member differs from the preceding one by a definite atomic grouping, is called a *homologous series*. The chemical properties of the members are very similar, but the physical properties vary continually from the smallest to the largest, according to molecular weight and complexity of branching of the carbon skeleton (see Table 11-2). To exemplify the Geneva system let us write a structural formula and then derive a name for it. If we increase the number of carbon atoms in the molecule beyond those given in Table 11-1, we find that the names are based upon the Latin word for the number of carbon atoms. Thus, a molecule with the empirical formula $C_{10}H_{22}$ is a decane. But there are several structural isomers, and it is patently unfeasible to name them in the manner in which the pentanes were handled. Let us consider one of the branched-chain isomers, and develop the Geneva system name for it:

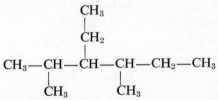

The placement of the side chain carbon atoms above or below the principal chain is of no consequence, since it is known that the atoms are free to rotate around a single bond, that is, a bond made up of one pair of electrons. The first step in naming this compound is to pick out the longest chain of carbon atoms. If we draw the molecule with the hydrogen atoms omitted,

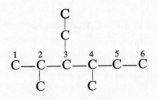

Table 11-1

Name	Empirical Formula	Structural Formula
Methane	CH_4	
Ethane	C_2H_6	
Propane	C_3H_8	
Butane	C_4H_{10}	
Isobutane	C_4H_{10}	
Pentane	C_5H_{12}	
Isopentane	C_5H_{12}	
Neopentane	C_5H_{12}	

Table 11-2   Physical Properties of some Straight-Chain, Saturated Hydrocarbons.

Name	Boiling Point (°C)	Melting Point (°C)	Formula
Methane	−162	−183	CH_4
Ethane	−89	−172	C_2H_6
Propane	−42	−187	C_3H_8
Butane	−0.5	−135	C_4H_{10}
Pentane	36	−130	C_5H_{12}
Hexane	69	−94	C_6H_{14}
Heptane	98	−90	C_7H_{16}
Octane	126	−57	C_8H_{18}
Nonane	151	−54	C_9H_{20}
Decane	174	−29	$C_{10}H_{22}$
Tetradecane	251	5.5	$C_{14}H_{30}$
Tetracontane	. . . .	81	$C_{40}H_{82}$

we number the chain from the end closest to the first side chain. Since the chain contains six atoms, we give the molecule the basic name "hexane." The side chains are indicated by the number of the carbon atom to which they are attached, and by the number of atoms in the side grouping. The side group name is derived from the name for the hydrocarbon with the same number of carbon atoms, but with the suffix -yl substituted for -ane (Table 11-3). The hydrocarbon minus one hydrogen atom is called a *radical,* but it must be noted that these radicals differ from inorganic ones in that they have no electrical charge.

The compound for which the formula is given (p. 73) is then named 2-methyl-3-ethyl-4-methylhexane, or better, 2,4-dimethyl-3-ethylhexane. From this name, we can draw one and only one corresponding structural formula.

Table 11-3

Hydrocarbon		Radical	
Formula	Name	Formula	Name
CH_4	Methane	CH_3—	Methyl
C_2H_6	Ethane	C_2H_5—	Ethyl
C_3H_8	Propane	C_3H_7—	Propyl

11-2   Petroleum and Petroleum Processing

It should be noted that all of the compounds named so far belong to the same homologous series, the *saturated,* or *paraffin,* hydrocarbons. These molecules are distinguished by the fact that only single bonds exist between carbon atoms, with each remaining bond site occupied by a hydrogen atom. These compounds make up the major fraction of petroleum, and range from gases methane and ethane to the solid waxes with carbon chains of twenty or more atoms. Natural gas is a mixture of methane, ethane, and propane; and bottled gas (LPG—liquefied petroleum gas) is propane or butane. The preferred molecular size for gasoline is eight carbon atoms in a highly branched arrangement, although commercial products are mixtures of isomers which include both longer and shorter chains. However, a small molecule has too low a boiling point, which means loss by evaporation, too rapid burning (engine knock) and loss of power. By the same token, larger molecules, with a higher boiling point, are vaporized incompletely and are equally ineffective as fuels for the internal combustion engine.

The first step in the processing of petroleum is fractional distillation. By this process, the temperature is increased gradually and fractions of increasingly high boiling point are collected (Table 11-4). The larger molecules

Table 11-4   Petroleum Fractions

Fraction	Size Range	B.P. Range (°C)
Gas	C_1–C_5	(−160)–(−30)
Petroleum ether	C_5–C_7	30–90
Gasoline	C_5–C_{12}	30–200
Kerosene	C_{12}–C_{16}	175–275
Fuel oil	C_{15}–C_{18}	250–400
Diesel oil		
Lube oils, Greases	C_{16}–up	350–
Paraffin waxes	C_{20}–up	M.P. 50–up
Residues (pitch, tar)		

are then subjected to a process known as catalytic cracking. Under high temperatures and pressures, and in the presence of a catalyst, the long chains break into smaller ones:

$$C_8H_{18} \rightarrow C_4H_{10} + C_4H_8$$

This reaction is typical of what might happen. Actually, the result is a mixture of a number of compounds of varying sizes. The proper selection of reaction conditions can result in the formation of a mixture in which the C_4 fragments predominate. Different conditions may give more C_2 molecules. The choice is determined by the synthetic processes which are to follow.

11-3   Unsaturated Hydrocarbons

The molecules produced are not all of the paraffin series, but may contain one or more double bonds. Such molecules are called *unsaturated,* and the names of the homologous series containing one double bond are given the suffix *-ene*. The molecule 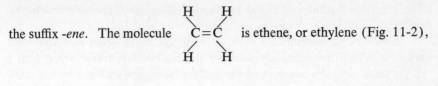 is ethene, or ethylene (Fig. 11-2),

Fig. 11-2. Two representations of the carbon-carbon double bond in ethylene. (From Brown, General Chemistry, Charles E. Merrill Books, Inc., 1963, p. 426.)

and H—C—C—C=C is butene. If two double bonds are present, the mole-

cule is a diene: C=C—C=C is butadiene. The fragments produced may

be combined into molecules of a size appropriate for gasoline, or they may be transformed into such diverse products as ethyl alcohol, polyethylene film and synthetic rubber.

The unsaturated hydrocarbons are much more reactive chemically than are the saturated ones. When a saturated hydrocarbon enters into a reaction, the bond existing between carbon and hydrogen, or carbon and carbon, must be broken and another formed in its place. There must actually be two bonds formed since two atoms were involved in the bond which has been broken. Reactions of this type may be characterized as *substitution reactions*, and an example is the reaction of chlorine with ethane:

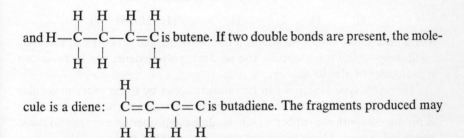

The compound produced could be named either ethyl chloride or chloro-ethane.

Reactions of unsaturated hydrocarbons are more often *addition reactions,* in which the relatively unstable double bond is transformed into a single bond, and the valences of the carbon atoms are satisfied by the addition of the other reactant:

$$
\begin{array}{ccc}
\overset{\displaystyle H \quad H}{\underset{\displaystyle H \quad H}{C=C}} + Cl-Cl & \rightarrow & \overset{\displaystyle H \quad H}{\underset{\displaystyle H \quad H}{Cl-C-C-Cl}}
\end{array}
$$

11-4   Polymers and Polymerization

Perhaps the most interesting type of reaction that involves the unsaturated hydrocarbons is that of polymerization. In the presence of a suitable catalyst, two molecules of ethylene will react to form a four-carbon molecule containing one double bond. This is accomplished by the transfer of a hydrogen atom from one molecule to another, with the subsequent joining together of the two bonds thus left unsatisfied:

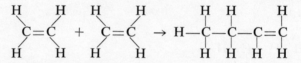

As the new molecule also contains a double bond, the process can continue indefinitely—until it is stopped. The product, polyethylene, can be produced in molecules of almost any size.

The same type reaction can be brought about by using other molecules as a starting material. The investigation of such reactions began with efforts to produce a synthetic rubber which would have properties superior to those of natural rubber. Many years ago the discovery was made that the viscous sap of the rubber tree could be vulcanized and made practically useful by heating it with elemental sulfur. Subsequent investigation showed that the raw rubber was a polymer of the five-carbon compound isoprene.

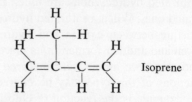

Isoprene

Since isoprene has two double bonds, the polymer formed from it still possesses some degree of unsaturation since, in the act of joining together, only one of the two interacting molecules lost its double bond:

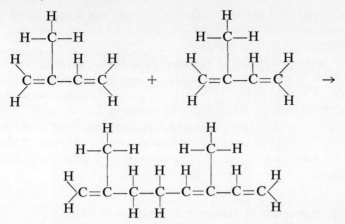

This process could continue, of course, and the resulting polymer would have double bonds along its length. As indicated previously, these double bonds are quite reactive, and the hardening of the rubber by vulcanization results from the formation of rigid covalent bridges of sulfur atoms between the

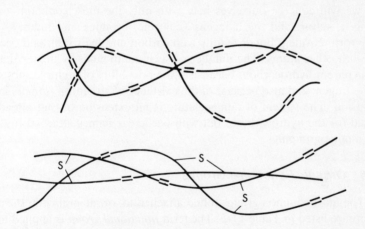

Fig. 11-3. Schematic representation of vulcanization of naturally occurring polyisoprene to produce commercially useful rubber. Sulfur atoms, or short chains of sulfur atoms, connect the polyisoprene chains, imparting hardness and greater elastic strength.

polyisoprene chains (Fig. 11-3). One of the most successful of the synthetic rubbers has been the polymer of butadiene.

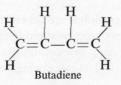

Butadiene

It can be polymerized and cross-linked in the same way as can natural rubber, but the qualities of the primary polymer molecules can be controlled, which is not possible with natural rubber.

The relatively short life of rubber articles in the Los Angeles area can be explained by the presence of double bonds in the molecular structure. Ozone, O_3, is formed in the atmosphere by action of sunlight on some of the pollutants from industry and automobile exhausts. This variation of the element oxygen is a very strong oxidizing agent, and can react with rubber to increase the number of cross-links between adjacent polymer chains. The result is the formation of a more rigid structure, with subsequent hardening and cracking.

11-5 Compounds with Elements in Addition to Carbon and Hydrogen

A great number of organic compounds contain only carbon and hydrogen, but their number is still small compared with those that contain one or more additional elements. Only a few elements are found to any great extent, and we will concern ourselves here with only the most common: oxygen, nitrogen, sulfur, and the halogens (chlorine, bromine and iodine). All of these form covalent bonds readily with carbon and hydrogen, and occasionally with other atoms. The number of such compounds is greater than that of the parent hydrocarbons because of the possibility of multiple substitution for hydrogen, and also because of the existence of structural isomers in great profusion. The system of nomenclature is an extension of that already discussed for the hydrocarbons, but with particular names attached to distinctive atomic groupings.

11-6 Organic Functional Groups

The most common groups found attached to, or integral with, the carbon chains are listed in Table 11-5. The term *functional group* is applied to them because they give to the compounds that include them, certain chemical and physical properties characteristic of the group and not of the total molecule. However, since organic molecules may be of very great size, there may be many of the same groups or even a great variety of different ones in the same molecule.

11-7 Polar Functional Groups

Perhaps the greatest single difference between the hydrocarbons and their derivatives containing various functional groups is in water solubility. Molecules containing only hydrogen and carbon are nonpolar and so are only very slightly soluble in water. The polar water molecules have no tendency

Table 11-5

Organic Functional Groups	
Formula	**Name**
—O—H	hydroxyl (alcohol)
$-\overset{\displaystyle O}{\overset{\displaystyle \|}{C}}-$	carbonyl
$-\overset{\displaystyle O}{\overset{\displaystyle \|}{C}}-O-H$	carboxyl (carboxylic acid)
$-N\overset{\displaystyle H}{\underset{\displaystyle H}{\Big\langle}}$	amino (amine)
$-\overset{\displaystyle \|}{\underset{\displaystyle \|}{C}}-O-\overset{\displaystyle \|}{\underset{\displaystyle \|}{C}}-$	ether
$-\overset{\displaystyle O}{\overset{\displaystyle \|}{C}}-O-\overset{\displaystyle \|}{\underset{\displaystyle \|}{C}}-$	ester
$-\overset{\displaystyle O}{\overset{\displaystyle \|}{C}}-\overset{\displaystyle H}{\underset{\displaystyle \|}{N}}-$	amide
$-\overset{\displaystyle O}{\overset{\displaystyle \|}{C}}-O-\overset{\displaystyle O}{\overset{\displaystyle \|}{C}}-$	anhydride
$-\overset{\displaystyle \|}{\underset{\displaystyle \|}{C}}-X$	halide
(X may be Cl, Br, I, or F)	

to form bonds of any kind with the hydrocarbons so that the latter are not dispersed by the solvent. Certain of the functional groups listed in Table 11-5 contribute some polar character to the molecule to which they are attached. Since the carboxyl group is acidic and the amino group is basic, these compounds will dissolve readily in dilute bases and acids, respectively.

Small polar molecules such as methyl and ethyl alcohols (CH_3-OH and CH_3-CH_2-OH) are completely miscible with water. However, as the length of the hydrocarbon chain to which the functional group is attached increases in size, the effect of the polar hydroxyl group on the molecule diminishes. The solubility of alcohols rapidly decreases with increasing carbon chain length so that pentyl alcohol ($CH_3CH_2CH_2CH_2CH_2OH$) is almost insoluble in water. The same effect is noted with the organic acids, all of which contain the carboxyl group. Of course, if these acids were relatively strong ones, they would ionize, and the negatively charged group would have an even greater effect in increasing solubility than does the polar hydroxyl. Even here, however, if the carbon chain is sufficiently large, the nonpolar portion of the molecule is effectively excluded by the water molecules. An interesting application of this fact is the use of alcohols of intermediate size (10 or 12 carbon atoms) to reduce the loss of water by evaporation from reservoirs in dry climates. These alcohols have a density less than that of water and, since they are insoluble, they float on the surface. The polar portion of the molecule is hydrated by the attachment to it of water molecules, so that instead of droplets of alcohol forming on the surface, the molecules are aligned in a monomolecular film. A cross section through the surface can be pictured as shown in Fig. 11-4, in which the rectangle represents the hydrocarbon chain,

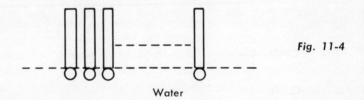

Fig. 11-4

Water

and the circle the hydrated hydroxyl group. The closely packed alcohol molecules, held in place by the interaction with the water molecules, have effectively eliminated the air-water interface at which evaporation occurs. This system is effective so long as there are no air currents strong enough to disrupt the surface film.

11-8   Soaps and Detergents

The action of soaps is analogous, although in this case the dispersibility of the organic compound is enhanced because of the presence of an ionized group. Soaps are sodium and potassium salts of long chain fatty acids. The fatty acids are so named because they form, as esters of the trihydroxy-alcohol glycerol, the fats and oils of animals and plants. The negatively charged acid ion is strongly attracted by the water molecules, but the long carbon chain (16-18 atoms) is excluded. This chain, however, may and does form bonds with other non-water soluble molecules or particles, which are then floated away by suspension in the water. Soaps have been replaced in large measure by the so-called synthetic detergents because of the inconvenience resulting from the formation of soap scums. Most natural waters contain calcium and magnesium ions in solution, and the salts of these ions with the fatty acids are insoluble. Some synthetic detergents are derivations of fatty acids in which the carboxyl group has been replaced by an ion which does not form insoluble salts with other ions in solution. Others have carbon chains which are not linear but may be branched or even contain closed ring systems. Unfortunately, these are not susceptible to attack by the micro-organisms which are found in surface water. As a result these compounds gradually increase in concentration in streams and rivers, until the water becomes unusable for ordinary purposes.

11-9   Molecules with Closed Ring Structures

The closed ring systems to which reference was just made form a group of compounds as large as that of the linear chain substances. It is common to distinguish the ring compounds as *aromatics,* while the chain molecules are referred to as *aliphatics.* The use of the word aromatic originated because the first of these materials which were characterized and identified had distinct odors, and, while we now know that this is not a necessary consequence of the presence of a ring structure, the classification is still a convenient one. Actually, the cyclic compounds are divided into two groups according to the identities of the atoms included. The *carbocyclic* compounds are those in which all of the constituent atoms making up the ring are carbon, while the *heterocyclic* include other atoms.

The properties of the carbon atom, both the tetravalent character and the tetrahedral structure, determine the nature of the carbocyclic ring compounds. The smallest of the closed molecules is cyclopropane, in the past commonly employed as an anesthetic. Cyclic structures including as many as eighteen carbon atoms were synthesized more than fifty years ago, but the most common are those containing six atoms. The six-membered ring has a greater inherent stability because the angles of the bonds between the carbon atoms are nearer to normal than are those in smaller molecules.

The carbocyclic compounds may be saturated or unsaturated, just as is true with those in which the carbon atoms are linearly bonded. It is of considerable interest to the chemist that the unsaturated benzene structure is not very reactive even though there are three double bonds in the molecule. In the middle of the 19th century it was known that the molecular formula for benzene was C_6H_6, but no structural arrangement for the atoms could be devised which would allow for the total number of valence bonds and at the same time account for the passivity of the compound under conditions which would give rise to rapid reactions for doubly and triply bonded carbon atoms. History now tells the story that the German chemist Kekulé dreamed of a ring arrangement during an afternoon nap. Whether the story is apocryphal or not, he did draw a structure that adequately described the molecule:

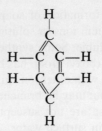

He went even further and proposed that the double bonds are not normal ones. Instead he hypothesized that there were neither single nor double bonds, but rather a resonating structure in which the electrons were evenly distributed throughout the entire molecule. Much later it was demonstrated by X-ray techniques that his postulation was correct, because the carbon atoms are at distances from each other which are too short for single bonds but too long for double bonds.

Many compounds have more than one ring, ones in which individual atoms, or pairs of atoms, form part of two rings. Naphthalene, the commonly used mothicide, has the formula $C_{10}H_8$ and a structural arrangement as follows:

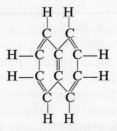

Some of the molecules recently implicated in cancer production, the carcinogens, have an even larger number of fused rings. Dibenzanthracene is an example:

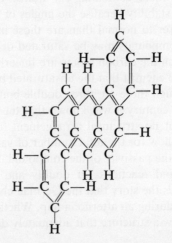

The mechanism by which these substances give rise to changes in cellular growth patterns is not understood, but it is believed that the activity is in some way related to the spatial arrangement of the atoms in the molecule and not to chemical characteristics.

11-10   Rings with Atoms Other Than Carbon

In addition to the carbocyclic compounds there are a great number of others whose ring structure includes atoms of elements other than carbon. These heterocyclic substances most commonly contain nitrogen, while oxygen and sulfur are found less frequently. These molecules may have either five- or six-membered rings, and, once again, there may be single or multiple systems. Examples of these are numerous (Fig. 11-5), and we will see that they are of great significance in biological systems.

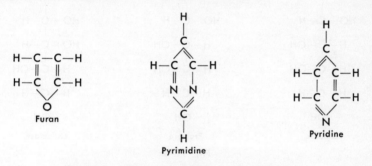

Fig. 11-5.   **Some typical heterocyclic molecules.**

11-11   Compounds of Biological Origin

As might be expected, compounds of biological origin and interest form a vast spectrum of the types of organic molecules. Quantitatively three groups, carbohydrates, lipids (fats) and proteins, far overshadow all the rest. These compounds play structural as well as functional roles in living organisms, so that they make up the bulk of the cellular material. Because of the amount of material available for study and by virtue of their obvious roles, these materials were known and investigated first. In addition, because these are the molecules that are oxidized to provide the energy necessary for the growth and reproduction of animals, it was easy to assess their function.

11-12   Carbohydrates

The carbohydrates are a group of compounds whose name is derived from the formula that expresses the simplest ratio of the atoms present in the molecule. These substances contain only carbon, oxygen, and hydrogen in relative numbers 1, 1, 2, so that the general formula can be expressed as

(CH₂0)—literally hydrates of carbon. If we look at the functional groups attached to the carbon chain, we find that the carbohydrates can be described as polyhydroxy aldehydes or ketones. The most common of these carbohydrates is the sugar glucose, which has a six-carbon chain and is a pentahydroxy aldehyde. There are two other commonly occurring simple carbohydrates with six-carbon atoms—fructose and galactose. Fructose contains a ketone group as contrasted with the aldehyde structure of glucose and galactose. The latter two differ only in the spatial arrangement of the atoms which make up the molecule. The formulas of all three are shown in Fig. 11-6.

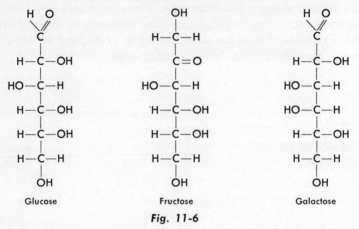

Fig. 11-6

The simple sugars can be formed into large molecules through the linking together of the smaller units with the loss of a molecule of water. Sucrose, the ordinary table sugar, is a compound which contains one glucose and one fructose unit joined together. The sugars such as glucose and fructose are called *monosaccharides,* and actually exist in a ring structure formed by a shifting of the bonds in the molecule. The *disaccharides* are formed by the union of two monosaccharides. One molecule of water is lost in the formation of the bond that exists between the simpler units which make up the larger molecule:

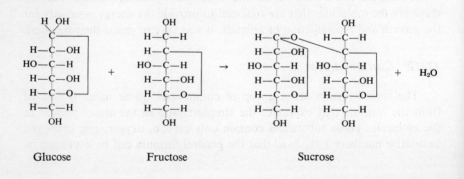

Molecules such as glucose and fructose are monosaccharides, and sucrose is a disaccharide. Even though a great many such structures are possible, living things produce only a limited number. Glucose occurs most often, although it is found in the polymerized rather than the free state. Vegetable starches, cellulose and the animal starch glycogen are all composed of glucose units linked in fashions related to that shown for sucrose. The fact that some are digestible while others are not is accounted for by the spatial configuration of the bonds between the molecules. Many very complex polymers contain molecules other than sugars. These are often found as structural members in cell membranes in animals and cell walls in plants or distributed in the extracellular fluids.

11-13 Amino Acids and Proteins

Another group of molecules which are found widely distributed in the biological world are the amino acids. Their similarity arises from the presence in each molecule of a carboxyl group and an amino group attached to the same carbon atom. Of all of the possible structures only about 20 are found to occur naturally, a situation brought about by the character of the cells which produce them. The type formula for the amino acids is

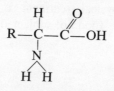

where R represents the carbon chain which identifies the particular amino acid. Just as with the sugars, the amino acids are found most often polymerized instead of in the free state. The amino acid polymers, known as *proteins,* are formed by joining two molecules together through the amino group of one and the carboxyl group of the other. A molecule of water is

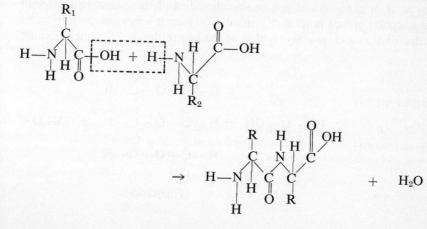

removed in the process. The process can be continued indefinitely because the molecule so formed still has a free amino group and a free carboxyl group. The bond between the amino acid residues is known as a *peptide bond;* the compound formed through the combination of two amino acids is called a *dipeptide.*

Proteins differ from each other both in their content of amino acids and in the sequence in which the residues occur in the extended chain. Because the R side chains have a variety of functional groups, the proteins differ widely in both chemical and physical properties. These molecules are so large that they must be classified as colloids, and are hydrated and dispersed rather than dissolved in water. Many proteins are not dispersible—those of hair and skin for example—and these can be shown to exist as extended chains bonded to each other in a variety of ways.

There are a great many proteins which in native state are folded into a compact, elongated spheroid by bonding between the amino acid residues in the chain of a single molecule. These bonds are relatively weak and are easily broken, so that the molecule can be transformed from the native form by a process termed denaturation. This is an irreversible process, analogous to the fate of Humpty Dumpty, and almost invariably results in the precipitation of the denatured protein, as is evident in the changes that take place when an egg is cooked or egg-white is beaten. Even the "nonsoluble" proteins are affected by physical treatment so that cooked food is easier to chew and to digest than is food not subjected to high temperature in a moist atmosphere.

11-14 Lipids

The third major category of the compounds of biological origin is a catchall which includes molecules of a great many types—the *lipids.* All are characterized by one property: that of being insoluble in water but soluble in nonpolar organic solvents. There are, to be sure, certain lipids which contain polar or even ionized groups, but the effect of these as contrasted with the nonpolar groups is relatively small. The largest subgroup, both in terms of distribution and quantity, is that of the neutral lipids, so named because

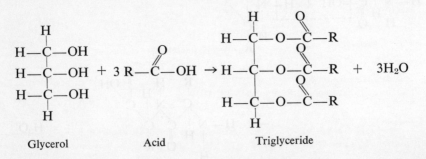

Glycerol   Acid   Triglyceride

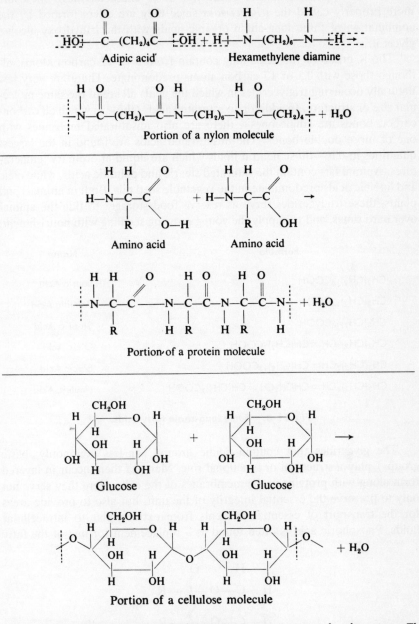

Adipic acid   Hexamethylene diamine

Portion of a nylon molecule

Amino acid   Amino acid

Portion of a protein molecule

Glucose   Glucose

Portion of a cellulose molecule

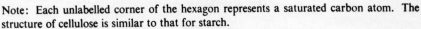

Note: Each unlabelled corner of the hexagon represents a saturated carbon atom. The structure of cellulose is similar to that for starch.

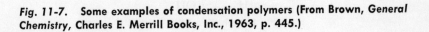

Fig. 11-7. **Some examples of condensation polymers (From Brown,** *General Chemistry,* **Charles E. Merrill Books, Inc., 1963, p. 445.)**

the molecules possess neither acidic nor basic characteristics. These are more properly called the *triglycerides* since they are esters formed by the combination of three long-chain organic acids with the trihydroxy alcohol glycerol.

The R group of the acids may contain from 3 to 17 carbon atoms, although those with 15 or 17 carbon atoms predominate. There are very few naturally occurring triglycerides in which the acids all are of the same molecular size or structure. In addition to saturated acids (those in which all carbon-carbon bonds are single ones), there are also unsaturated molecules with one or more double bonds. The unsaturated acids are found in the largest quantities in oils—those neutral lipids which are liquid at ordinary temperatures. Animal fats contain the saturated stearic and palmitic acids, while oleic and linoleic acids predominate in the vegetable seed oils. Both in animals and plants, these triglycerides serve as reserve food storage: to tide the animal over hard times, and to supply the young growing seedling with nourishment.

Formula	Name
$CH_3(CH_2)_{10}COOH$	Lauric Acid
$CH_3(CH_2)_{14}COOH$	Palmitic Acid
$CH_3(CH_2)_{16}COOH$	Stearic Acid
$CH_3(CH_2)_7CH=CH(CH_2)_7COOH$	Oleic Acid
$CH_3(CH_2)_7CH=CH(CH_2)_{11}COOH$	Erucic Acid
$CH_3(CH_2)_4CH=CHCH_2CH=CH(CH_2)_7COOH$	Linoleic Acid

Fig. 11-8.   Some long-chain fatty acids.

The glycerides that contain acidic groups (or less commonly, basic groups) play a structural or functional role. Many of them occur in layered form along with proteins in the membranes of the cells. Here they serve not only to preserve the essential integrity of the unit, but also to provide areas for the transport of essential nutrients from extracellular to intracellular fluids. Phosphoric acid is often found as a replacement for one of the fatty

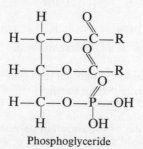

Phosphoglyceride

acids, and provides a reactive site which allows the reaction of the glyceride with carbohydrates or proteins.

11-15 *Vitamins and Hormones*

The vitamins and the hormones are two groups of organic compounds which are classed as they are because of their functions, and not because of any similarities in their chemical structures. The carbohydrates, proteins and lipids act both to provide the organism with oxidizable foodstuff and also to contribute structural elements. The vitamins are necessary in very small quantities and are important because they participate in certain reversible chemical reactions. These may be equilibria in the process of the oxidation of foodstuffs, or in the synthesis of body constituents; they will be considered in the next chapter. It should be noted that the vitamins are divided into two large groups on the basis of a single physical property: solubility. The B-vitamins and ascorbic acid (vitamin C) are soluble in water, but vitamins A, D and E are insoluble. The latter three are soluble in lipids, and are found dissolved in the body fat and seed oil of animals and plants, respectively. This difference in solubility accounts for the fact that certain vitamins are stored in the body in relatively large quantity while others are not. The large quantity of fat in the animal body can act as a storage area for fat-soluble materials, but the constant and rapid turnover of the water content of the organism makes it impossible to accumulate stores of water-soluble materials.

The same situation exists for the hormones, another group of organic molecules which play functional roles, as it does for the water-soluble vitamins. These compounds have diverse chemical natures but are grouped together because they are produced and distributed in a related fashion. The hormones (from the Greek, "to arouse or excite") are elaborated at special sites and are secreted into the blood stream for distribution to those cell systems or organs whose activity the hormones affect. The specific mode of action is much less well understood for these compounds than for the vitamins, but we will see in the discussion to follow something of the role both play in the chemical functioning of living organisms.

QUESTIONS FOR STUDY AND REVIEW

1. The number of isomers possible for the homologous series of saturated hydrocarbons increases drastically as one goes up the series. For hexane, C_6H_{14}, there are five; and for octane, C_8H_{18}, there are fifteen. No mathematical formula has been derived to predict the number of isomers to be expected.
   (a) Draw the structure for each isomer of hexane.
   (b) Name these isomers according to the Geneva system of nomenclature.
   (c) Do the same for all the possible heptanes, C_7H_{16}.

2. Upon combustion in an excess of air, all organic compounds yield carbon

dioxide and water. How many volumes of air are needed to burn one volume of butane gas? (Air is about one-fifth oxygen)

3. From the formulas for the hydrocarbons given in Table 11-1, what general formula would seem to cover all cases? What then will be the formula for dodecane, which has twelve carbons? Unsaturated compounds have pairs of hydrogens missing from the formula. What general formula would fit there?

4. Polymers have been produced in great variety. One of them, polyethylene, has already been mentioned in the text. Another, known as Orlon, results from the polymerization of a substance called Acrylonitrile, $CH_2{=}CH{-}CN$. What structure would Orlon have?

5. Ducks can float because their feathers are coated with a film of grease so that air is trapped within the feather layers. If a small amount of organic compound known as an emulsifier is added to the water, the ducks sink forthwith. What kind of properties does an emulsifier have?

6. The poor housewife is bombarded with the virtues of various brands of soaps and detergents. However, considering the way that soap does its work, are soap suds beneficial? Would detergents be more effective than soaps? How does the color of the soap affect the process?

7. For a long time compounds like ether, $C_4H_{10}O$, and cyclopropane, C_3H_6, were used as anesthetics. The results were occasionally disastrous, however. Physiological difficulties aside, why has the use of these compounds in anesthesia been curtailed?

Chapter 12

Biochemistry

The preceding pages have been concerned with the chemistry of the compounds of carbon, molecular species which are in large measure identified with living things. It is time now to consider the reactions which produce certain of these compounds and, as well, the manner in which these substances are metabolized to provide the energy which makes life possible. In the preceding chapter we saw something of the complexity of organic chemistry—a condition which exists because of the large number of compounds that can be formed from a small number of elements. At the same time it was pointed out that all of the laws and theories discussed in earlier chapters applied without exception to this area of chemistry. Our study of chemistry would be incomplete if we did not consider, at least briefly, some of the reactions that take place in living organisms, since such dramatic advances are being made in the application of chemical principles to biological systems.

12-1 Photosynthesis

The ultimate source of energy for all of the living organisms on the face of the earth is the sun. The radiation from that body is absorbed by green plants, and, through the process known as *photosynthesis,* is used to build up energy-rich molecules, which are subsequently ingested by animals. All animals are supported, in the last analysis, by energy derived from the sun. Photosynthesis can be defined as the process of the combination of inorganic compounds into organic molecules through endothermic reactions for which the energy comes from solar radiation. The overall transformation which occurs can be written as

$$6CO_2 + 6H_2O \rightarrow C_6H_{12}O_6 + 6O_2$$

where the product is identified as the monosaccharide glucose. As is so often the case, this equation is a drastic oversimplification, but it is useful because it demonstrates some very important relations. Glucose does represent the principal end product, although it is seldom found in the free state in any organism. It is either polymerized to form starch, or it is metabolized to provide the energy for other endothermic reactions by which essential cellular constituents are synthesized from elements, ions, or small inorganic molecules. Equally importantly, this equation indicates the manner in which the status quo is maintained between the photosynthetic plant world and those animals whose existence depends upon an available supply both of oxygen and oxidizable foodstuffs. The equation as written is endothermic; its reverse is exothermic. The complex molecules formed are oxidized by animals through reaction with oxygen, which is the other product. We will not concern ourselves here with the particular reactions involved in the process of the fixation of carbon dioxide; that is, the sequence of interactions which results in the formation of oxygen as well as glucose. The interdependence of the plant and animal kingdoms is evidenced by the fact that the carbon dioxide liberated by the oxidative process is the starting material for photosynthesis, and that oxygen is released in the series of reactions which occur.

12-2 Digestion and Metabolism

If we consider the chemical reactions which are involved in the growth and maintenance of an animal, we find that all of them are included in the processes of *digestion* and *metabolism*. Digestion we apply to those reactions which occur within the gastrointestinal tract—really external to the organism—while we reserve metabolism for the totality of the reactions which take place within the cells and body fluids. Digestion can also be defined as the breaking down of foodstuffs into fragments of assimilable size, while metabolism includes both oxidative (energy-producing) and synthetic reactions. Before we can discuss in detail any of the numerous reactions that take place in a living system, it is mandatory that we consider the mode of action of the molecular species which direct and control those reactions.

12-3 Enzymes: Biological Catalysts

Enzymes are materials which are generally described and defined as biological catalysts, and are further characterized as being protein in nature. In previous discussion both catalysts and proteins have been considered in some detail, but it behooves us now to be precise in our usage of these terms when they are applied to a single chemical species. In so doing, we will not consider more than a very small fraction of the total number of reactions that take place, but rather will deal with hypothetical examples of that group of compounds which represent the class "enzyme."

In the beginning, we must reiterate what has been said before—that a catalyst can do no more than speed up the rate of a reaction which is thermodynamically possible under the existing circumstances. The enzyme has no special qualities in this regard. There is no vital force which distinguishes the chemical reactions of a biological system from those of the inorganic world. Indeed, as we delve more deeply into the investigation of biochemical reactions, we will see more and more clearly that the same rules are obeyed as were originally laid down for inanimate systems. Let us introduce some new symbolism and certain new concepts, and discuss briefly the manner in which an enzyme mediates in the on-going process of metabolism in a biological system. To do so we must introduce one new term. The *substrate* in an enzymatically controlled reaction is the compound of interest which enters as a reactant into the system and which in an altered form appears as a product of the reaction.

Let us consider a reaction in which a substrate, S, is converted to a product, P, through the intermediation of an enzyme, E. The reaction could be written simply as

$$S \xrightarrow{E} P$$

where the role of the enzyme as a catalyst is noted by its being associated with the arrow which indicates the direction of the reaction. This is, however, an oversimplification. We would be more correct if we wrote the reaction as

$$E + S \rightarrow ES \rightarrow E + P$$

so that the true role of the enzyme catalyst is unequivocally demonstrated. The first step in the reaction is the combination of enzyme and substrate to form a complex molecule which subsequently breaks apart to form the product and the regenerated free enzyme. The enzyme itself, it should be noted, differs from the inorganic catalyst with which it is compared in that the enzyme is not a stable entity. The complexity of its structure and the dependence of its biological activity upon both its chemical character and its physical configuration, makes it very susceptible to irreversible alteration. Any protein can be denatured, and the enzyme is no exception. Most importantly, denaturation of an enzyme results in a complete loss of its biological activity, since its ability to moderate a reaction depends upon the external configuration of the molecule.

12-4   The Mode of Action of Enzymes

As indicated previously, a protein is produced through the joining together of a large number of amino acid molecules. The combination takes place in such a fashion that the side chains are not involved in the bonds that hold the molecule together. Accordingly, the properties of the protein are the summation of the physical and chemical properties of the groups which extend from the central chain. More importantly, the long chains of the pro-

teins can and do bend upon themselves to form ellipsoidal dispersible colloids, in which case only a small number of the amino acid residues are on
the outside of the molecule. The enzymatic activity of a particular species
can then be related to its physical configuration. Each enzyme is specific in
that it mediates reactions which involve either one specific substrate or a
particular class of compounds. The accepted explanation for this experimental observation is that the enzyme and substrate must fit together in a
lock and key arrangement if any interaction is to take place. A schematic
presentation of this is found in Fig. 12-1.

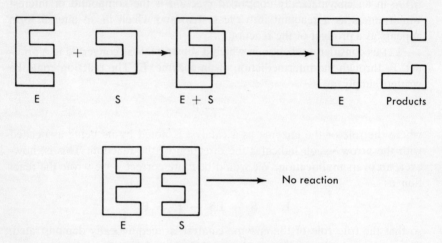

Fig. 12-1.   Enzymatic reaction and inhibition.

It is interesting to note in this regard that molecules which approximate
the configuration of the substrate, but which cannot, for structural reasons,
undergo the chemical transformation (from reactant to products) that is
characteristic of the substrate, act as inhibitors for the action of the enzyme.
These molecules are sufficiently like the substrate that they combine tran-
siently with the enzyme, thus effectively reducing its concentration. This type
of inhibition is important in many instances of antibacterial and even cancer
chemotherapeutic action.

12-5   The Process of Digestion

Now that some basis for understanding the action of enzymes has been
established, let us follow the course of ingested foodstuffs through the process
of digestion. Cooking serves to initiate the breakdown of a variety of structures to make the large molecules more susceptible to attack. Because chemical interactions do not take place unless the molecules concerned are in very
close proximity, it is necessary to break up the particulate matter into much
smaller units. These are then acted upon by the enzymes secreted in mouth,

stomach, and intestine until the colloidal molecules of carbohydrate and protein are converted into water soluble monosaccharides and amino acids, and the water insoluble lipids are broken down into soluble acids and alcohols. These reactions, all hydrolytic in nature, are only slightly endothermic, and the normal temperature of the body is sufficiently high that the reaction proceeds easily. Reactions that are classed as involving *hydrolysis* are those in which a covalent bond is split by the concomitant dividing of a molecule of water and the introduction of the fragments to substitute for the previously existing covalent bond. The three major types of hydrolytic reactions involve proteins, carbohydrates, and lipids. The enzymes which catalyze these reactions are named after the substrate upon which they act, with the characteristic suffix *-ase* appended. In some instances the names are very general, for example *proteinase* and *lipase;* but in others they are somewhat more specific, as *amylase,* the enzyme which hydrolyzes the starch (carbohydrate) fractions *amylose* and *amylopectin.* Certain enzymes, especially those of the digestive tract, have trivial and not systematic names. They were among the first active enzymes discovered, and were named long before their chemical nature was known. *Pepsin* and *trypsin,* the proteinases of the stomach and small intestine, respectively, are examples.

12-6   Intermediary Metabolism

When the foodstuffs have been broken down into fragments small enough to dissolve readily, the products of hydrolysis are absorbed and pass into the blood stream. At this point our concern switches to the area of intermediary metabolism, that vast complex of chemical interactions taking place within the cells of the body. The maintenance of life depends upon oxidation reactions which can be controlled to produce energy in a usable form. If the reactions took place as they do in inorganic systems, that is, with the direct evolution of energy as heat, they would patently be useless. While the liberation of a certain amount of heat is often necessary for the regulation of body temperature, this control is more often achieved by the utilization of the heat produced as a side-product in metabolic processes. The metabolic patterns that have evolved satisfy the two general requirements: step-wise oxidation with the release of energy in small increments, and the direct transfer of such released energy from one chemical compound to another. These two criteria are satisfied by the existence of particular classes of compounds whose sole function is to mediate in the passage of chemical energy from one compound to another. Their molecular composition is such that they can absorb energy by undergoing chemical transformations, and then can be broken down to make the energy available for a variety of reactions which synthesize essential body constituents. These molecules also store energy in such a fashion that it is available for muscular contraction and the performance of work. It must be remembered that the animal body, like any other machine, is not 100% efficient. In every interchange some heat is liberated. The warm feeling that follows the ingestion of a good meal is an indication of this inefficiency. The transformation of ingested food into usable fuel is marked by the evolution of heat, and this heat accounts in part for the warm feeling that follows a full meal.

12-7   The Transport of Oxygen and Carbon Dioxide

As evidenced from the overall reaction for the oxidation of glucose, the functioning of the cells depends upon the maintenance of a constant supply of oxygen and the simultaneous removal of the carbon dioxide produced. This transfer is effected by the blood, specifically by the red cells and by the weak acids and bases in the plasma. The hemoglobin of the red cells is a complex protein that contains an ion of iron which is both ionically and coordinately bonded. This ion, bound into the organic molecule, has the capacity to attach through a coordinate bond one molecule of oxygen. During the passage of the blood through the capillary vessels of the lung, the hemoglobin becomes saturated with oxygen. The oxygen has passed by diffusion across the thin tissue layers separating the red cells in the capillaries from the air sacs in the lung itself. Characteristic of most reactions in the body, this is an equilibrium system, and the hemoglobin is almost saturated because of the relatively high oxygen concentration of the inhaled air.

When the blood is pumped to the peripheral capillary beds, it enters an environment in which the concentration of oxygen is much lower. As a result the equilibrium is shifted in the opposite direction, and oxygen is made available for the myriad oxidative reactions in the cells of the body. The carbon dioxide that is produced must be disposed of, and the systems in the plasma which are suited to this purpose come into play. Here again we find reactions for which the balance depends upon the relative concentration of one of the reactants. When carbon dioxide dissolves in water, the resulting solution takes on an acidic character according to the reaction:

$$CO_2 + H_2O \rightarrow H^+ + HCO_3^-$$

The tolerance of the body cells for H^+ ions is relatively low, and the excess produced is absorbed by a series of buffers that are found in the blood plasma and in the red cells. Two examples of these can be given, one of an organic and one of an inorganic nature.

Proteins, as has been indicated previously, contain side chains that possess both acidic and basic characters. We can depict these molecules as particles of colloidal size with both acidic (carboxyl) and basic (animo) groups attached. Both of these exist in equilibrium with H^+ ions:

$$R-\overset{\overset{\textstyle O}{\|}}{C}-O-H \ = \ R-\overset{\overset{\textstyle O}{\|}}{C}-O^- + H^+$$
$$R-NH_2 + H^+ \ = \ R-NH_3^+$$

When free hydrogen ions are introduced into the solution, the first equilibrium is shifted to the left while the second moves to the right. The net result is that most of the increase is absorbed so that the acidity of the solution does not change appreciably. The same circumstance holds for the inorganic system

$$HPO_4^{--} + H^+ \rightarrow H_2PO_4^-$$

By these devices, the carbon dioxide generated is dissolved and made transportable without undue disruption of the acidity of the body fluids. When the blood containing large quantities of dissolved CO_2 reaches the lung, the equilibria are shifted once again because the air in the air sacs has a low CO_2 content. Carbon dioxide then diffuses in the opposite direction to that taken by oxygen, and the product of combustion is then exhaled.

12-8 Metabolism without Oxygen

If, as occasionally happens, the body is forced to work at a rapid rate, the blood is not capable of transporting oxygen to the tissues fast enough to keep up with the metabolic reactions. In this case the cellular constituents follow a different metabolic path, one which is described as *anaerobic*. The prefix *a-* or *an-* means without, so anaerobic signifies life in the absence of air (or oxygen). The overall reaction which takes place then is simply a rearrangement of the atoms of one molecule into smaller units which have a lower energy content. This is not a simple one-step operation, but follows a complex pattern, since the requirement still exists that the energy released must be made available for the essential functions of the cells. In the animal body the reaction is

$$C_6H_{12}O_6 \rightarrow 2C_3H_6O_3 + energy$$

The reactant is glucose as before, but the product is the organic compound lactic acid:

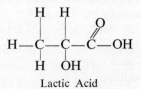
Lactic Acid

This compound is a stronger acid than is carbonic acid (CO_2 + H_2O), and so the acidity of the tissue fluids and the blood changes more drastically. The tired feeling that develops following violent exercise is in large part due to the accumulation of lactic acid in the tissues. A distance runner gets his "second wind" when his metabolic system reaches a balance so that oxygen is being supplied to the tissues at a rate consonant with that at which oxidation is proceeding. It might be noted parenthetically that most of us are familiar with anaerobic metabolism of another type. Ordinary yeast cells have the capacity to carry out a series of reactions in the absence of oxygen in which glucose is transformed into ethyl alcohol and carbon dioxide:

$$C_6H_{12}O_6 \rightarrow 2C_2H_5OH + 2CO_2$$

This is not a reaction which involves oxygen, but rather is a dismutation comparable to that which produces lactic acid. Of course, the production of lactic acid is not confined to animal cells. *Lactobacillus acidophilus,* the microorganism which sours milk, gives lactic acid as an end product. The bacterium responsible for producing yogurt, *Lactobacillus bulgaricus,* has as its metabolic end products other organic acids which impart a different flavor.

Of course, the oxidizable substrate in the cell need not be carbohydrate in nature. Both fat and protein are oxidized with the production of energy for cellular use, and, interestingly enough, by essentially the same mechanisms as are employed for the metabolism of carbohydrate. As we shall see later, there is no difference in the calories derived from carbohydrate, fat and protein once these are incorporated into the metabolic system. There are dietary differences, but these are psychologically or physiologically based and have no reference to the biochemical reactions at the cellular level.

12-9   The Steady State

One thing that needs to be noted at this point is the manner in which the overall composition of the organism remains unchanged even though reactions are taking place at a rapid rate. This condition is described as the dynamic state of body constituents, and the organism is characterized as being in a *steady state.* This is distinguished from a system at equilibrium by the fact that the steady state organism is constantly interchanging both matter and energy with its environment. A living system can never be in a state of equilibrium since there would then be an even distribution of energy throughout. In this circumstance action and reaction could not occur. There are many reversible chemical reactions which will come to equilibrium if isolated from the body in which they normally exist. Indeed it is the presence of these systems which makes the steady state possible, because any change at any point in the steady state—whether from the absorption of foodstuff or the performance of work—leads to a readjustment which re-establishes as closely as possible the original conditions. Of course, for most of us the steady state is only approximated, but still the body displays a remarkable constancy of composition.

12-10   The Disposal of End Products of Metabolism

We have already considered the manner in which the compounds necessary for growth and maintenance are taken into the body, and should look briefly at the excretory processes by which the end products are eliminated.

The liver plays a central role in the overall metabolism of the organism. Specific reactions take place in all cells for the synthesis of necessary constituents and for the making available of energy to meet local needs. It is the liver which transforms much of the ingested food into usable form, however, and this organ also acts as a storehouse from which the cells can be supplied on demand. Lipids, carbohydrates and amino acids, the latter obtained from protein, are to a large degree interconvertible. Supplies of all three in excess of immediate need are in part changed into glucose and stored as the polymer glycogen in the liver. In addition, fatty acids are synthesized in the liver, transported by the blood and stored in the tissues as neutral fat.

Certain cells in the liver carry out special reactions to detoxify compounds which are harmful. These altered materials are then excreted into either the intestine or urinary tract and so are removed from the body. Similar reactions serve to transform the metabolic products into innocuous water-soluble molecules which can be disposed of easily.

12-11 Overnutrition and Undernutrition

This discussion would be incomplete if some attention were not given to the question of the chemical composition of the diet which keeps a human organism functioning. It is not difficult to describe an ideal diet, but such a prescription is often not followed either because foods are not available, or because societal or personal habits or taboos eliminate certain items. Too often when we think of malnutrition there comes to mind only the spindly, pot-bellied, under-fed child of the tropics. Malnutrition properly considered must include both overnutrition and undernutrition, and it is the former which is of particular concern in the affluent societies. It is not at all difficult to get too much of good things, as is evidenced by the prevalence of obesity in the United States. It is comforting, but unrealistic to believe that one is fat because of some genetic inheritance, some malfunctioning of the metabolic system. There are a few instances of this, it is true, and there are also wide variations in the efficiency with which human bodies operate. One person gets fat on diet that barely supports another. For any one individual, however, getting fat is simply the end result of eating more food than is burned in exercise. A caloric imbalance results in the excess being transformed into fat which is stored.

Many diets have been devised to assist people to lose weight or to avoid gaining it. Some of these are good, but too many are crash programs which can do considerable harm. One of the mistakes which is all too commonly made is the acceptance of the notion that calories derived from protein differ from those which are supplied by carbohydrates. There is absolutely no basis for such an assumption. Under proper medical supervision caloric intakes can be drastically reduced for considerable periods of time. It is essential that any reduction in the quantity of food consumed still allow for the ingestion of an adequate supply of the essential nutrients, those molecular species which must be provided preformed to the body. In addition to the vitamins, these include certain amino acids whose synthesis cannot be accomplished by any of the cells of the body.

The individual who has no medical problems has no difficulty in choosing a diet that will keep him in good health. The administration of various supplemental materials is sometimes indicated, but the wholesale consumption of pills and panaceas is, all too often, profitable only to the manufacturer and the purveyor. An adequate diet includes a variety of foods, and one gets fatter or thinner according to the quantity eaten. It is true that excess calories are commonly supplied by carbohydrates, but it is unwise to attempt to eliminate carbohydrates completely from the diet. Overeating is often a question of too much carbohydrate because of the interesting physiological and psychological phenomenon which we know as satiety. The two common foods that can be eaten regularly in large quantity without the development of some feeling of revulsion are bread and potatoes, and these are predominantly carbohydrate.

A simple quantitative consideration can point out the significance of that last observation. Reference to any one of a number of cookbooks will supply the information that one slice of bread provides 75 calories, and it is also known that fat has a caloric value of 9 calories per gram. A simple arithmetical calculation will show that if for one year you eat one slice of bread per day over and above the dietary intake necessary for the maintenance of your present weight you will gain six pounds of body fat. Since the deposition of this quantity of fat in the body is accompanied by the simultaneous formation of other tissues, and the accumulation of body fluids, the weight gain will be greater. It seems safe to assume that eating one slice of bread less instead of more will result in a weight loss of the same magnitude. Unfortunately this rate of weight reduction is too slow for most of us, and there is also a requirement for a degree of self-discipline which is arduous in the extreme. We require something more dramatic, so we embark upon crash programs which promise much but which, in addition, may lead to severe dietary deficiencies. All that is really necessary is to leave the table still a little hungry—eat the same diet, but eat a little less. There is a folk-saying among those informed in the science of nutrition that is applicable. Paraphrased, it is that a man can get the exercise he needs by pushing himself firmly away from the table before the second helping. Of interest also is the observation, supported by experimental data, that the thin rats bury the fat rats. Extra weight may be of transient advantage, but in the long run it is detrimental.

There are many definitive treatises available on the subject of nutrition, and a host of others much better known which cater to the all too human desire to find the easy way out. It is not within the scope of this short discussion to present all of the facts and figures which allow a distinction to be made between the two. Let us only remember that the laws of chemistry apply to the functioning of the human body as they do the production of gasoline from petroleum. There are no shortcuts, no easy escapes from the workings of the chemical systems which govern the metabolism of each of us.

QUESTIONS FOR STUDY AND REVIEW

1. The carbon dioxide level in the earth's atmosphere has been found to be gradually increasing. How can this observation be explained?

2. Why is cooked food more readily digested than raw food? How does a meat tenderizer function to make a tough steak more tender?

3. Write reactions for the hydrolysis of proteins, carbohydrates and lipids.

4. What explanation is there for the fact that a man blacks out if he is suddenly transported from sea level to an altitude of 15,000 feet?

5. Contrast specifically between a system that is in a steady state and one at equilibrium. What characteristics, if any, do they have in common?

Glossary

Acid. A substance that produces hydrogen ions in aqueous solution; a substance that donates protons.

Activation energy. The extra amount of energy required in a collision to produce a chemical reaction.

Addition reaction. A reaction with an unsaturated compound in which one molecule adds to another to form a new molecule containing both.

Amphoteric. Capable of acting as either an acid or a base.

Atomic number. The number of unit positive charges carried by the nucleus of an atom.

Atomic weight. The weight of an atom relative to oxygen taken as 16.

Avogadro's law. Equal numbers of molecules are contained in equal volumes of all gases under the same conditions.

Avogadro's number. The number of oxygen atoms in a gram-atom of oxygen (6.012×10^{23}).

Base. A substance that liberates the hydroxide ion in aqueous solution; a substance that accepts protons.

Boyle's law. The volume of a gas at constant temperature is inversely proportional to the pressure.

Brownian motion. A continuous, random motion of tiny particles caused by collision with molecules.

Buffer. A solution to which large amounts of acid or base can be added with only a little resultant change in hydrogen ion concentration.

Calorie. The amount of heat required to raise the temperature of 1 gram of water 1°C.

Carbocyclic. Having a ringed structure containing only carbon atoms.

Carbohydrates. Naturally occurring compounds that are polyhydroxy aldehydes and ketones.

Catalyst. A substance that increases the rate of a reaction without being changed itself.

Catalytic cracking. Decomposition of heavy petroleum fractions under the influence of heat and catalysis into simpler molecules.

Centigrade scale. The scale of temperature in which 100° is the boiling point of water and 0° is the freezing point of water.

Charles' law. At constant pressure, the volume of a gas is directly proportional to the absolute temperature.

Chemical property. A property that relates to a substance's chemical reactions.

Colloid. A substance consisting of particles too large to be dissolved in solution but generally too small to be seen.

Component. One of the substances in a mixture.

Compound. A substance composed of atoms of two or more different elements.

Concentration. The amount of solute in a given amount of solvent.

Coordinate-covalent bond. A covalent bond produced when both electrons shared are contributed by one member of the pair of atoms.

Covalent bond. A bond formed by shared electron pairs.

Dalton's law. In a mixture of gases, the molecules of each kind exert the same pressure as they would if alone. The total pressure is the sum of these partial pressures.

Density. The weight (mass) of a material divided by its volume.

Diffusion. Spontaneous mixing of one substance into another.

Electrolyte. A substance that conducts electric current when dissolved in water.

Electrons. Subatomic particles of negative charge.

Electron shell. An orbit around the nucleus containing a characteristic number of electrons.

Electrostatic. Pertaining to forces caused by electrical charges.

Element. A substance whose atoms are all alike.

Endothermic. Taking in heat.

Enzymes. Protein substances whose biological function is to catalyze chemical reactions in cells.

Equilibrium. A condition in which the properties of a system remain constant with time; the reactants are forming products at the same rate products are forming reactants.

Equilibrium constant. A constant expressing the fact that when a reversible reaction has attained equilibrium, the rates of the forward and reverse reactions are equal.

Exothermic. Giving off heat.

Fahrenheit scale. The scale of temperature in which 212° is the boiling point of water and 32° is the freezing point of water.

Fractional distillation. Separation of components by boiling (distilling) the fractions off individually.

Gas laws. A description of the nature of the behavior of gases. See *Boyle's law, Charles' law, Avogadro's law,* etc.

Heat capacity (specific heat). The number of calories required to raise the temperature of 1 gram of a substance 1°C.

Heat of fusion. The amount of heat required to change 1 gram of a substance from the solid to the liquid state.

Heat of reaction. The quantity of heat evolved in the course of a chemical reaction.

Heat of solution. The quantity of heat evolved when a substance dissolves in solution.

Heat of vaporization. The amount of heat required to change 1 gram of a substance from the liquid to the gaseous state.

Heterocyclic. Having a ringed structure containing two or more different kinds of atoms.

Heterogeneous. Not uniform throughout.

Homogeneous. Uniform throughout.

Homologous. Containing a series differing by one number from one to the next.

Hormone. A protein substance that regulates certain cellular processes.

Hydration. The act of surrounding an ion or molecule with solvent water molecules.

Hydrolysis. Cleavage of a compound by the use of water.

Hydronium ion. A hydrated hydrogen ion, H_3O^+

Ion. An element or radical containing a net charge.

Ionic (electrovalent) bonding. Bonding via electrostatic attractions of oppositely charged ions.

Isomers. Molecules containing the same number of atoms of each kind but in differing spatial arrangements.

Isotopes. Atoms of an element whose nuclei contain the same number of protons but different numbers of neutrons.

Kinetic energy. The energy possessed by a substance because of its motion.

Law. A general statement correlating a large number of facts.

Law of Combining Volumes. Volumes of gases that react with one another do so in a ratio of small integers.

Law of Conservation of Mass and Energy. Mass and energy can neither be created nor destroyed.

Law of Definite Proportions. Different samples of a substance contain atoms in the same proportion.

Lipids. Fatty materials of large molecular weight containing ester and alcohol groups.

Mass. The amount or quantity of matter contained in a body.

Mass law expression. The rate of a reaction is proportional to the concentrations of the reacting masses.

Matter. All substances of which the universe is composed; that which has mass and occupies space.

Metals. Elements that tend to lose electrons when entering into chemical combination; that conduct electricity; are malleable; etc.

Mixture. A sample of matter containing two or more substances not chemically united.

Neutralization. The formation of water and a salt by the reaction of a base and an acid.

Neutron. A subatomic particle in the nucleus having a mass equal to that of the proton but devoid of charge.

Nucleus. The central part of the atom where the positive charge and mass are concentrated.

Oxidation. The gaining of oxygen; the loss of electrons.

Paraffins. The saturated series of hydrocarbons.

Perfect gas. One which follows the laws of Boyle, Charles, Avogadro, etc.

Period. A horizontal row of the periodic table.

Periodic law. Properties of the elements are not abritrary, but depend on atomic structure and vary in a systematic way.

Periodic table. An arrangement of elements illustrating the periodic law.

Physical property. A characteristic quality. See also *chemical property.*

Polar. Having unequal charge distribution so that the ends are oppositely charged.

Polybasic. Containing more than one proton replaceable by base.

Polymerization. The union of a large number of simple molecules to form a giant molecule.

Potential energy. The latent energy a substance possesses because of its position.

Pressure. Force acting upon a given area.

Protein. An amino acid polymer.

Proton. A subatomic particle of positive charge found in the nucleus.

Radical. In organic chemistry, a group containing one remaining valance which can be attached to a carbon chain; in inorganic chemistry, a group of atoms possessing a net charge.

Rate. The speed of reaction.

Rate constant. A proportionality factor resulting from the mathematical expression of the mass law.

Reaction. The process that converts one substance into another.

Reduction. The loss of oxygen; the gaining of hydrogen; the gaining of electrons.

Replacement reaction. A reaction in which one atom substitutes for another in a given molecule.

Saccharides. Sugars.

Salt. The ionic compound resulting from the neutralization of an acid and base.

Saturated. In organic chemistry, containing the maximum possible number of hydrogen atoms.

Shell. See *electron shell.*

Solute. The dissolved substance in a solution.

Solution. A homogeneous mixture of two or more substances.

Solvent. The component present in excess in a solution.

Steady state. An equilibrium situation in which the substance in question is being gained through one equilibrium as rapidly as it is being lost in another, and thus its state remains steady.

Structural formula. A two-dimensional representation of a three-dimensional chemical structure.

Sublimation. Direct passage of a substance from the solid state to the gaseous state.

Substance. A homogeneous species of matter of definite chemical composition.

Substitution reaction. See *replacement reaction.*

Valence. The combining power of an element.

Vitamin. A mixed class of compounds necessary to the body, which are catalytic in nature and which the body itself cannot prepare.

Vulcanization. The process of combining the unsaturation in rubber with sulfur to produce a strong, cross-linked compound having improved properties.

Index

Light Metals

I A   II A

PERIODIC CLASSIFICATION
OF THE ELEMENTS
(BASED ON $C^{12} = 12.0000$)
1961 ATOMIC WEIGHTS

Heavy Metals

VIII B

III B   IV B   V B   VI B   VII B

I A	II A	III B	IV B	V B	VI B	VII B		VIII B	
1 **H** 1.0080									
3 **Li** 6.939	4 **Be** 9.012								
11 **Na** 22.990	12 **Mg** 24.31								
19 **K** 39.102	20 **Ca** 40.08	21 **Sc** 44.96	22 **Ti** 47.90	23 **V** 50.94	24 **Cr** 52.00	25 **Mn** 54.94	26 **Fe** 55.85	27 **Co** 58.93	28 **Ni** 58.71
37 **Rb** 85.47	38 **Sr** 87.62	39 **Y** 88.91	40 **Zr** 91.22	41 **Nb** 92.91	42 **Mo** 95.94	43 **Tc** (99)	44 **Ru** 101.1	45 **Rh** 102.90	46 **Pd** 106.4
55 **Cs** 132.91	56 **Ba** 137.34	57 TO 71	72 **Hf** 178.49	73 **Ta** 180.95	74 **W** 183.85	75 **Re** 186.2	76 **Os** 190.2	77 **Ir** 192.2	78 **Pt** 195.09
87 **Fr** (223)	88 **Ra** 226.05	89 TO 103							

Lanthanide series	57 **La** 138.91	58 **Ce** 140.12	59 **Pr** 140.91	60 **Nd** 144.24	61 **Pm** (147)	62 **Sm** 150.35
Actinide series	89 **Ac** (227)	90 **Th** 232.04	91 **Pa** (231)	92 **U** 238.03	93 **Np** (237)	94 **Pu** (242)